THE FIRST TREASURE DIVERS

THE FIRST TREASURE DIVERS

THE TRUE STORY OF HOW TWO BROTHERS INVENTED THE DIVING HELMET AND SOUGHT SUNKEN TREASURE AND FAME

JOHN
BEVAN

An AquaPress Book
Published by AquaPress Ltd
25 Farriers Way
Temple Farm Industrial Estate
Southend-on-Sea
Essex SS2 5RY
United Kingdom

First Published 2010
AquaPress and the AquaPress Logo are Trademarks of AquaPress Ltd.

A CIP catalogue record for this book is available from the British Library.

For information on all other AquaPress titles visit www.aquapress.co.uk

ISBN 13: 978-1-905492-16-9
ISBN 10: 1-905492-16-2

Contents

Part One
Breathing Fire and Water

I
Sweepers and smugglers

The tiny sailing boat was being tossed around like a helpless rag-doll in the jaws of an enraged sea. As the full moon slid from behind black stormy clouds it shed its cold light on a bearded old man wrestling desperately with the boat's hefty tiller. The water draining from his oilskins and sou'wester hat glistened in the moonlight before flying sideways down wind. Though half-blinded by the stinging salty spray, he was frantically trying to keep the boat's head pointing into the breaking waves. If the boat was thrown sideways onto the waves it would be capsized in seconds. His arms were locked around the tiller, which fought to throw him bodily from one side to the other. His two sons, similarly dressed in bulky oilskins and heavy sea boots, struggled to tie down the remnants of their torn sail, which whipped about as if lashed by a vengeful devil. Each wave that crashed over them threatened to wash them overboard.

Huddled in a corner, near the hatchway to the deck below, a shivering young mother clutched a tiny baby to her bosom. She was shivering as much from fear as from the cold. Her long dark hair and shawl were strung out in the wind. She dared not look up because she knew the sight was too horrific. Even so, she couldn't help noticing the water rising in the cabin below deck. She was preparing to die a cold and cruel death, together with her baby, two brothers and father.

They had been returning from a routine trip to Ramsgate, running swiftly with the tide along the Kent coast to Gravesend. It was a journey the three men had made many times before though it was the first time for the mother. It should have been plain sailing but the wind had suddenly veered and increased from the west. Wind blowing against the tide is a lethal combination, which whips up tempestuous seas. It was made even worse by the shallowness of the waters that flowed between the treacherous sandbanks. The old man cursed to himself for having missed the warning signs and having let himself be caught in such a simple trap. The ominous clouds had gathered on the horizon, signalling the approaching gale but the light had been failing and he had been too preoccupied with his daughter and baby grandson to notice them. Then darkness had fallen and by the time he saw them coming it was too late. He was committed to the journey and there was no turning back.

They could see occasional lights on the shore, a mile distant.

They were even close enough to smell the rotting seaweed that festooned the beaches, but they may as well have been in the middle of the ocean. They were all alone, disappearing into the deep troughs between the roller-coaster waves. They knew it would not be long now, before the end came.

But then, the boat suddenly mounts the crest of a rolling wave and one of the sons catches a glimpse of another vessel's faint light off their port bow. He points disbelievingly and calls out to his father. Each time the boat climbs to the top of a wave they all strain their eyes to search the darkness for redemption. Barely audible voices shout out through the howling wind and spray. A small sailing boat, a cutter, appears out of the gloom and approaches across the mountainous waves. With uncanny skill, the cutter manoeuvres alongside and a coiled rope is thrown across. The two sons grab the rope as it snakes through the air, quickly run it around a cleat and throw the end back to the rescue boat. The two boats wallow and grind menacingly against each other despite the rope fenders put out by the rescue boat. Splinters fly as the sides of the two boats clash and start to break up.

At the tiller of the rescue boat stands George Bell, one of the most capable boatmen on the Kent coast. He shouts to one of his crew, John Deane, and orders him to grab the girl who is being supported by her two brothers ready to jump across. John's strong arms reach out and the mother and child are heaved unceremoniously aboard. Ordered by their father, the two sons obediently follow next. They leap across with youthful agility despite their cumbersome clothing, skidding as they land on the cutter's lurching deck but managing to catch hold of some rigging.

Now only the father is left. He is still fighting with the tiller.

Everyone shouts at him to jump, but he has to time his move carefully. If he gets his timing wrong he will never make it and his own youthful agility had long since disappeared. So he waits anxiously for the opportune moment. When the two boats are pitching almost in unison, he seizes his chance. He abandons the tiller and lurches for the side of his boat. But just then the crazily swaying masts of the two boats collide above him. There is a sickening cracking sound and the boat's broken mast-top and rigging come crashing down on top of the old man, knocking him to the deck. Dazed and momentarily pinned down under the loose rigging, he raises his bleeding head and looks helplessly across to the rescue boat. He raises a hand and tries to say something but just then a large wave breaks over him. When the water has drained away, he is no longer there.

For a moment, all on the rescue boat are stunned. They can only stare at the empty boat. They desperately scan the boiling seas for any sign of the old man, but he has disappeared. The sons call out in vain but there was nothing they could do for him. The sea had taken him and he had gone to a watery grave.

The rope is let go and the cutter pulls away just as the sailing boat begins to founder. Its timbers creak, crying in agony as the boat slips slowly beneath the insatiable waves. Below deck on the rescue boat, the two young sons do their best to comfort the sobbing mother whilst the boat's crew go about their well-practised duties. John Deane and two of George Bell's brothers, James and William, haul on the ropes, skilfully and silently setting the sails for the homeward journey. The survivors are too shocked, cold and exhausted to speak. They just embrace each other for warmth and comfort with what strength they have left, and grieve for their lost father. The cutter sails on through the darkness and heavy seas back towards its home town of Whitstable. As the boat's stern rears up over the top of a wave, a shaft of moonlight picks out its name, *Providence*.

An anxious crowd is holding a silent vigil on the beach, awaiting the safe return of their heroic loved ones. They are the families and friends of the elite group of Whitstable boatmen who had acquired the unlikely title of the *Sweepers*. The noise of the gusting wind and the waves pounding on the shingle makes it impossible to have a meaningful conversation. Several dogs sit obediently alongside, peering and blinking into the darkness. They would be the first to spot the returning boat, barking excitedly as soon as they sensed the boat's imminent arrival. The group huddles closely together, holding their flickering oil lamps aloft to help guide their boat back to safety.

Such was a typical rescue mission undertaken by the courageous sweepers of Whitstable in the treacherous waters of the Thames estuary. Its unseen shoals readily whipped up precipitous waves in response to wind over tide. The estuary suffered chronically from extreme mood swings. One moment it was a haven for shipping, the next, a graveyard. The Whitstable sweepers knew it well. They often included a dog in their boat's crew, and it had a most important duty. It would be stationed up near the bow, and using its innate instincts together with its enhanced sense of hearing, it could tell when the boat was nearing dangerously shallow water. It could pick up the smallest change in the sound of the waves over shallow water, well beyond human capability, and that would set it off barking loudly. Many a boat had been saved from almost certain disaster by the prompt intervention of its faithful sea dog.

The Whitstable sweepers would go out in almost any weather. They had no fear of drowning. Many of them subscribed to the concept that a man who was born to hang could never drown. If they weren't saving souls they would be salvaging cargo, or even boarding an abandoned East Indiaman and sailing her back to sheltered water. These were occasional financial windfalls in reward for their intrepid endeavours whenever they could claim salvage on a vessel or its cargo. Unfortunately, they were not frequent enough to live by, but they certainly provided a welcome boost to the local economy.

Whitstable is a small, seaside town nestling on the north coast of Kent. In the 1820s the community relied almost entirely on farming its historic and rich oyster beds as a source of employment. The "Royal Whitstable Natives" as the local oysters are called, to this day enjoy an excellent reputation attributed to the unique quality of the brackish water on that part of the coast. Harvest time is roughly between October and February, when the sea is at its coldest, but it can extend either side so long as there is an "r" in the month. Then the boats would regularly fill their holds from the holding tanks in the oyster store and sail up the river Thames to the fish market at Billingsgate, in the heart of London. There they found a ready sale with the eagerly awaiting oyster merchants. Ten to fifteen million native oysters a year joined in this one-way journey.

The oyster business was a jealously guarded one, which can be traced back over 2,000 years to Roman times, and even beyond. If you weren't in one of the oyster families, there was little hope of your getting a share of it. Not, of course, unless you married into it or your eldest son was invited to take on a seven-year apprenticeship when he reached the age of sixteen. The industry was retained and protected by a privileged group of local families supported by the full authority of an Act of Parliament obtained in 1793. The Act enabled the incorporation of The Company of Free Fishers and Dredgers of Whitstable, which strictly regulated the fishery. The Company elected a Water Bailiff who policed the fishing activities with a rod of iron. He had ultimate authority and his position was treated with the very greatest respect. He regularly imposed heavy fines for a variety defined irregular practices. Stealing oysters carried a maximum penalty of transportation to Australia for seven years. For a serious legal dispute, they would call in a heavy-duty lawyer from London, sparing no expense. Nothing was more important than the protection of the rights and privileges of the oyster fishermen.

The trade was supported by a fleet of about a hundred sailing boats that anchored just off the beach, each boat belonging to a different family. The boats were all of the same type but they were variously called cutters, smacks or yawls. They had a deck and one mast. They were versatile, seaworthy, and well suited to coastal work and trading. Many often journeyed far afield, across the English Channel and into the Mediterranean Sea.

Other traditional sources of employment thrived in the town, such as boat building and sail making. A series of busy boatyards with their long straight slips running down into the sea were strung out along the long shingled beach.

Coastal trading was a growing industry in the 1800s and coal was the main commodity, not just for heating and cooking but also to help feed the growing numbers of hungry steam powered engines. Whitstable spritsail barges, brigs and brigantines regularly sailed up to Newcastle, loaded up with coal, and delivered it to coastal towns on their return journey, with Whitstable itself being a major recipient. It was the main port supplying the bustling, ancient city of Canterbury.

But in the 1820s, Whitstable did not yet have a purpose-built harbour. To get their cargoes ashore, the boats had to beach at high tide and then wait for the tide to go out. Then horse-drawn carts rumbled over the sea wall at a point known as the Horsebridge and down the shingle to the waiting boats, now sitting high and dry. It was a laborious and time-consuming process.

The trading reached across the channel to Holland, Belgium, and of course France in particular. Indeed, the market for French brandy was blossoming, even though it was strictly illegal. Just about every boat owner around the south of England dabbled to a greater or lesser extent in smuggling.

The Preventive Service, the forerunners of the Customs and Coastguard, tried their best to stop the illicit trade but they were run ragged and usually outwitted by the guile and devious skills of the local boatmen. A little bribery and corruption also helped to grease the wheels of this black economy.

Finally, if a family couldn't penetrate any of the established trades, there was always the business of sweeping and salvage. This is where the most skilled and entrepreneurial boatmen were found. They were by necessity, nature's survivors. They lived off their wits, and they had the strength, resolve and raw courage to eke a living out of adversity. It is these adventurous Whitstable boatmen who supply one of the essential ingredients of the story of the diving helmet.

Whilst salvaging from the not-infrequent shipwrecks in the Thames estuary offered an important income to the boatmen, it provided neither a regular nor reliable source of revenue. But as luck would have it, there was one more, lucrative activity to exploit in the shallow waters, in-between shipwrecks.

The south side of the Thames estuary provided a spacious and convenient anchorage for vessels trading in and out of London. Hundreds of sailing vessels were anchored off Whitstable at any one time. Some would be waiting for a berth up-river, or perhaps a fair wind or convenient tide before proceeding to London. Others would be waiting for the right wind or tide to head off round the coast, either north, or south into the channel.

If Lady Luck smiled on the Whitstable sweepers, a northerly gale would blow up.

Several hundred vessels then had an urgent choice to make: ride the gale out at anchor and hope the anchor holds, or weigh anchor and set sail to ride out the gale at sea. It wasn't an easy choice and it was always a gamble. It is no wonder that the anchor has become a symbol of "hope".

For those who chose to stay, there was the ever-present danger their anchor might drag or the anchor cable could even snap. They could lose their ship, their cargo and worse still, their lives. They could be drowned or dashed to pieces on the shore. But if the anchor did begin to drag, they had one final option - they could cut and run. At least then they saved themselves and their ship, though they did sacrifice their main anchor and its cable.

And this is where the Whitstable sweepers came in.

Abandoned anchors and their cables presented a rich harvest to be reaped from the seabed all along the coast when the gale had passed by. The anchor recovery boatmen even had their own title, the Sweepers of Whitstable, and they formed a sort of fraternity. They were fiercely competitive but staunchly united against their common enemies of poverty and the Preventive Service. There was no question about it, they were the experts at finding and recovering abandoned anchors. That was their stock in trade and it was their daily routine. When no other more lucrative prospects were in the offing, they would be out there, methodically and patiently sweeping for anchors.

The usual sweeping arrangement was for two boats to sail on a parallel course, dragging a weighted line, the sweep, on the seabed between them. An anchor fluke sticking up from the sandy bottom provided the perfect snag for the line. Then came the really skilful part. They next had to manoeuvre their boats in such a way as to wrap the sweep around the anchor and secure it. Then a block and tackle would be attached to the sweep and in a series of hoists, the heavy anchor would be hauled to the surface over the bow of their boat.

This was hard labour and not without risk. Fingers and hands could become trapped in the rigging as the boat rocked about, snatching sharply at any loose ropes. At worst, the considerable weight of the swinging anchor could swamp or capsize the boat. Great care was required in manhandling a salvaged anchor to the surface and securing it to the side of the boat in preparation for the hazardous trip back to sheltered water.

They had other tricks of the trade up their sleeves. If they had to work alone, they could simply haul a special grappling chain, known locally as a creep, behind their boat, which could snag an anchor cable lying flat on the seabed. Once caught, it could be hauled to the surface and the anchor cable itself used to hoist up the anchor. But working alone was less likely to succeed. Two boats offered more manpower for the heavy hauling, there was safety in numbers and the sweep was more efficient at snagging anchors than a creep.

Indeed, their skills at recovering items from the seabed were so highly developed that they were occasionally applied to smuggling French brandy. After returning from a shopping trip to France, the boatmen first called in to a secluded bay, out of sight of the Preventive Service. The illegal cargo of brandy barrels would be weighted down, strung together in a line and then lowered to the seabed like a string of lobster pots, except there were no floating buoys attached to the ends to mark their position. The whole point was that they would be undetectable on the surface.

They fixed the location of their illicit hoard precisely by noting the relative positions of conspicuous features on the shore, such as identifiable rocks lining up with prominent trees or perhaps a conveniently placed windmill or church spire. When the boat finally came ashore, the Preventive Service would meet an innocent, sober crew and not a trace of brandy on the vessel. At dusk the boatmen would set out again to sea, returning to their carefully fixed position where they would lower their creep to pick up the line of barrels waiting safely on the seabed.

Under cover of darkness, the boat, now loaded with brandy, would head for a predetermined point on the shore, well away from the Preventive Service patrol. They would be guided to the precise point on the shore by a trusted friend holding a special lantern, covered all around except for a narrow vertical slit, so its thin beam of light would only be visible from directly offshore. Not a glint of light would escape in any other direction to betray his position. The more imaginative smugglers would have arranged a diversion a little further along the coast to lure the patrol away from their secret rendezvous. As if by magic, family members and friends would suddenly appear from the shadows and silently form a well-rehearsed human chain down the beach to help unload the brandy barrels as swiftly as possible. Within minutes the barrels would be tucked away, safe and sound, in a secret cellar under one of the houses that lined the beach. Many of these secret cellars still exist today.

When the Preventive Service returned hot foot from their wild goose chase, they knew perfectly well that brandy had just been smuggled ashore, but they also knew they were unlikely to find out where. Over the ensuing weeks the brandy would be distributed to customers all around town and to all levels of society.

A heavily laden horse-drawn coal-cart making its regular round of deliveries would pull up to a house. A young lad would jump down from the cart and take up his position holding the horse by its bridle. He appeared bored with his chore and looked lazily about. The weary coalman would begin to carry the heavy sacks of coal to the house, On one of his returns to the cart he would exchange a knowing nod of the head with the young boy, signifying the coast was clear. Then a brandy barrel would miraculously appear from the cart's false bottom and disappear quickly through the back door - one more satisfied customer.

When ships carrying valuable cargoes sank nearby, the boatmen appeared swiftly at the scene. Finding the wreck was usually quite easy, because the tops of its masts usually stuck up, out of the water. Then they quickly set to work at recovering the freight. They used a variety of special tools attached to the ends of long poles. There were devices for cutting and breaking up the deck of a sunken ship and to open up the hold. Other devices were designed for grasping the cargo, such as pincers, grapples and hooks. Their ingenuity at clearing the holds of sunken vessels was quite amazing.

So these were the various ways in which the Whitstable Sweepers went about their challenging business. But who exactly were in this unique and exclusive fraternity?

Their core members consisted of a large family that hailed from Herne Bay, an even smaller town than Whitstable about five miles east along the coast. This was the rough tough Bell family. They had generated a large number of accomplished nautical artisans over the past three generations. There were fathers, sons, uncles, nephews and cousins. They were resourceful, hard-working and adventurous men who had no chance of breaking into the heavily protected oyster fishing business, so they developed their boating skills for salvage. They had to, to survive. The Bells also produced some eligible daughters several of whom married well, into the wealthy oyster fishing, ship owning and ship building Gann family of Whitstable.

As well as assembling boat crews from suitable family members, the Bells also recruited carefully selected local mariners who were equally enthusiastic, resourceful, skilled, and above all, could be trusted. One of these was the twenty-two years old John Deane of Deptford. He had become a close friend of George Bell whilst they had both been serving their seven-year apprenticeships on the East Indiamen, trading between London, India and China. George was very popular with his companions though he was a bit of a rebel at heart and he didn't respond too well to authority. On one of his trips with John Deane to Madras and Bengal he had to be "confined in irons" for "mutinous language and refusing to do his duty" when ordered by the Boatswain. He had always been a bit of a wild character and in amongst the extensive Bell family, he was always the one in the most trouble.

On one occasion, back in Whitstable, he was recognised amongst a group of men who were pounced upon by awaiting Preventive Service officers just as they were unloading sixty gallons of smuggled French Brandy ashore at night. The group instantly dropped their booty and scattered into the town's dark alleyways, every one of them making a successful escape. But George was eventually hauled up in front of the local magistrate and the Preventive Service officers claimed they had clearly recognised him as one of the smugglers. But then about a dozen witnesses came forward and declared on oath that George had been with them, a long way away at the time. The Magistrate had no choice but to acquit him and George narrowly escaped being transported to Australia.

John Deane on the other hand was altogether more sensible and if anything, had a stabilising influence. Tall, powerfully built and bounding with energy, he fitted in well as he enjoyed the adventurous sea-life of a salvager. He had become, to all intents and purposes, a member of the Bell family. John was readily inspired by the enthusiasm of the others. He enjoyed the challenge, being part of a team and developing new skills. If he had a fault, it was that he was far too trusting. He gave his loyalty easily and completely. He would help anyone in trouble. He found it difficult to recognise or even believe the plots and devious ways in unscrupulous people. Despite his worldly travels, there was still a certain naive innocence about his outlook on life.

1832 was a very important year for Whitstable. This was when the new harbour was opened and it had a huge impact on the local communities. It set off an explosive expansion in trade and sent out a new wave of optimism throughout the county of Kent. An enormous crowd attended the grand opening ceremony in March. The whole town turned out and several thousand visitors swelled the numbers to nearly 10,000 souls.

The land-locked city of Canterbury was the main beneficiary. It now had its own port, and there had always been a chronic shortage of harbours on the north Kent coast. A regular steam packet service was quickly established between Whitstable and London, carrying passengers and cargo up and down the Thames estuary. Coupled with the new steam railway which had opened between Canterbury and Whitstable two years previously, Whitstable became the key port through which both commuters and commodities trafficked between London and Kent. The Canterbury to Whitstable railway is amongst the first in the world. As well as coal, the railway was used extensively to supply the fishmongers of Canterbury with fresh fish, oysters, crabs and winkles. The carriages inevitably acquired a powerful fishy smell and contributed to the line being dubbed the "Crab and Winkle Line".

The trading restrictions between Britain and Europe had been lifted since the decisive Battle of Waterloo and the end of the Napoleonic War, just a few years previously. Europe was beginning to enjoy a period of relative peace with the dawn of *Pax Britannica*. Harbour towns like Whitstable inevitably benefited.

Several members of the Bell family had moved to Whitstable from Herne Bay to take advantage of the new harbour facilities. They set up in business and established an international reputation for their salvaging prowess. Needless to say, they handled their prowess at smuggling a little more discreetly.

Four Bell brothers in particular, formed the principals of the group. Each was the master of his own sailing cutter and they formed an unbeatable team. James who was the eldest (44) had the cutter *William & Alice,* William (39) had the *Perseverance,* George (37) had the *Providence*, and Wallace (34), the *Prosperous*. So great was their prowess and reputation that underwriters at the Society of Lloyds in London, the largest insurance market in the world, would contract their services directly. Lloyds would send them all around the country and even to Europe to attempt to recover valuable cargoes from shipwrecks. They even received commissions from as far afield as France.

But this salvaging service had its limitations. Whilst their skills were amongst the best available in the country, they were still quite primitive. By its very nature, the cargo recovery process was destructive. It involved working blindly from the surface, using crude tools, tearing wrecks apart and then grabbing randomly amongst the unseen debris for the valuable cargo. Much of it was missed, damaged or even lost in the process.

Necessity was crying out for a more efficient means of reclaiming the cargo. If a new salvage technique was going to be invented, the chances were that it would be in Whitstable.

2
Sunken Treasure

HMS *Lutine* had struck a sand bank off the island of Terschelling, Holland, during a gale in October 1799. The doomed ship had been on her way to Hamburg from Yarmouth with a cargo of over £1,000,000 in gold bullion aboard, all of which was underwritten at Lloyds of London. Out of the two hundred passengers and crew on board, only one passenger survived the tragedy. It was such a major human and financial disaster that when the *Lutine's* bell was later recovered, it was hung up in the Underwriters' room in Lloyds and traditionally rung whenever a ship's loss was reported. It hangs there to this day.

She was originally a French thirty-two gun frigate called *La Lutine*. But when Admiral Hood relinquished Toulon to Napoleon Bonaparte in 1793 she was one of twelve frigates he took with him as prizes. Hood sailed them to Gibraltar where they were commissioned in the Royal Navy and *La Lutine* became HMS *Lutine*.

The Bells became acquainted with the sinking of the *Lutine* through their frequent meetings with underwriters at Lloyds and in 1823 they decided that the *Lutine's* treasure should be their next big prize. The wreck was in shallow water, some of her timbers even showed above the sea bed as the sands shifted up and down the coast. The treasure was tantalisingly only a few feet away, and it was there for the taking.

What could be simpler?

The Bells negotiated with Lloyds who in turn negotiated with the Dutch government. An agreement was eventually drawn up in July 1823 between Lloyds, the Dutch, and the Bell brothers. Since the Bells had been brought up as seafarers without any formal education, William Whorlow, who was a shipping agent at Whitstable, acted as their agent.

The four brothers staked all they had on the venture. They loaded up their four cutters with supplies and their special tools and optimistically sailed out of Whitstable harbour into the North Sea, heading for Terschelling. James led the way on the *William and Alice*, followed by George on the *Providence*, William on the *Perseverance*, and Wallace on the *Prosperous*. Their crews totalled thirty seamen in all, with John Deane serving with his old friend George on the *Providence*. If fortune smiled on them, they would all be fabulously rich men by the time they returned. Their expectations could not have been higher.

At Terschelling, whenever the weather permitted, they dug away feverishly at the sea bed in the shallow waters all through the summer season using pincers, scoops and poles with sacks on their ends. They tried everything they could think of, they worked themselves to the bone, but despite all their efforts not one thing of any value was recovered. At the end of the summer, they returned to Whitstable with nothing to show for a whole season's work. Their families were devastated. It was a financial disaster.

However, they were still convinced that they could be successful eventually, if only they could keep up the search. They tried to renew their contract in 1824 but the Dutch government had been unimpressed with the previous year's results and had lost faith in their capabilities. The Bells were informed in no uncertain terms to stay well away. In fact, if they did return, they were warned they would be shot at! It was just as well because they needed the time to recoup their outlay on the previous year's fruitless project.

The Bells were so adamant that they could ultimately find the *Lutine's* elusive treasure, they sustained their attempts to persuade the Dutch to let them have one more try in 1825. Against the odds, they somehow got what they wanted. They spent another entire summer season working in the shallows with their poles but once more their best efforts resulted in no significant finds. They were so near, yet so far from untold wealth! As far as anyone knows, the majority of the treasure is still there, frustratingly just a few feet under the sand. Perhaps we should call it a sand bank.

Translated into English, *Lutine* means "tormentress", so the ship was at least living up to her name. It was extremely frustrating. If only they could get down there and get their hands on the wreck, instead of having to work blindly, from the ends of poles. There had to be a better way.

The Bells all but bankrupted themselves with the *Lutine* venture. It was back to anchor sweeping if they were to be able to continue to feed their growing families. That was the salvage business - one minute you were up, the next, you were down. As ever, the Bells survived and somehow pulled through. A sprinkling of wrecks in the Thames estuary provided them with a little help to repay their debts and rebuild their financial resources. They also expanded their repertoire into raising entire ships. In 1826 they raised a vessel laden with iron and towed her back to Whitstable.

They were still searching for the big breakthrough when serendipity played a card.

The Pearl Fishery Company of Ceylon (now Sri Lanka) had decided to experiment with the use of small diving bells to increase their productivity in harvesting shells and pearls. They had commissioned the famous civil engineer George Rennie in London to build them a couple of small bells. The technology was hardly new, diving bells had been around for at least three centuries. But it was only in relatively recent times that pumps had been developed that could supply the bells with air from the surface. Rennie was already in the bell manufacturing business having supplied large cast iron bells to several major ports and harbours around the country. The first pearling bell was sent out to Ceylon and following extensive trials, the Fishery decided it was not a good idea after all. So they cancelled the order for the second bell and it was put up for sale in London.

This bell looked like an upturned dustbin, but it was wider at the open bottom end than at the top. When lowered into the water with its open end lowermost, it trapped a volume of air inside. A man could stand on a sort of trapeze suspended underneath the bell with his head and chest up inside, in the air bubble. A manually operated air pump at the surface continuously supplied fresh air down a hose to the bell so the diver could remain there as long as he wished.

The unexpected availability of this bell at a knock-down price was an opportunity that the Whitstable family couldn't afford to miss. So a sale was agreed and the Rennie bell became the Bell bell. At last, they could get direct access to the seabed. They could be freed from being tied to the surface, working blindly with poles. Now they could get their hands to work directly on the wrecks. John Deane in particular couldn't wait to try it out.

The first opportunity to put their new bell to work came in 1828. The French government commissioned them to recover a cargo of copper from the brig *Hermione* sunk in the river Seine. After a few diving training sessions and familiarising themselves with hoisting the bell, they sailed across the channel with high hopes. But by the time they arrived at the wreck in the Seine they discovered the cargo of copper had already been liberated by the locals. They had managed to get into the hull when the tide had fallen and helped themselves to the copper ingots. Just like so many salvage ventures, it proved another costly failure.

True to the names of their vessels, they put their trust in providence and persevered. But would that ever make them prosperous?

It was critically important that they proved the utility of their new bell as soon as possible. So they looked around closer to home for a suitable wreck. The obvious choice was the wreck of the East Indiaman *Hindostan* which had foundered off Margate during a storm in 1803. Twenty of her crew had been lost in the tragedy. She was a 1,248-ton, 38-gun vessel and she had been loaded with gold, silver and copper destined for India when she had gone down. As always, the project was another big gamble. They were speculating desperately they might find something that would have been buried deep inside a deep, dark and decayed wreck that was broken up and sunk into sand. They were also in dangerous, unpredictable waters with fast-flowing tides. But they were not deterred. Using their diving bell was the only way they could physically get their hands on the wreck. Whatever needed to be done would have to be done.

Whilst the diving bell offered important advantages, it did not come without its own, inherent risks to life and limb. Its operation demanded great care and skill. A mistake could easily cost a life.

Heavy weights had to be attached to the bottom of the bell to overcome the buoyancy of the large volume of trapped air and to get it to sink. This meant that when it was out of the water, the bell was horrendously heavy. It weighed almost a ton. Slung from the bow of the boat, it would swing ponderously and not only risk damaging the boat's hull by collision but also introduced the possibility of capsizing the vessel if the water was rough. The operation was very weather-sensitive and could only be undertaken in the calmest of sea conditions. And how often did that happen? Furthermore, if the current picked up, it could sweep the bell and its diver away like a leaf in the wind. The manpower required to raise and lower the bell when it was out of the water was considerable. A special winch had to be installed on the boat to lower and raise the bell and its operation was painfully slow.

John was the first to volunteer to go down in the bell. Thankfully he had no feelings of claustrophobia as he climbed inside the small bell that so terrified some of his colleagues. They had panicked the moment they had put their head inside and swore *nothing* could persuade them to dive in it. They didn't believe that anyone could possibly undertake such a perilous and terrifying mission.

As they lowered the bell, one of the first things that John noticed was the sudden silence that fell on him the moment the bottom of the bell touched the surface of the sea. The acoustics in the bell were instantly transformed and his own voice echoed loudly back to him. The regular beats of hissing air being pumped into the bell became the dominant sound. It suddenly became quite dark and the water beneath him glowed unnaturally green. This was surely an alien world he was daring to enter.

A signal rope was paid out from the boat as the bell descended. It ran down under the edge of the bell and up inside where John held tightly on to the other end, ready to signal in an emergency. He tied it around his wrist to make sure he didn't lose it. As the bell descended, the increasing pressure of the water squeezed the bubble of air and the water level started to rise disconcertingly up inside the bell. This problem slowly went away as more air was pumped down to him, though the men on the surface found it much harder to pump as the pressure inside the bell increased with the depth.

John next experienced a piercing pain in his ears as he continued his descent. It has been variously described by earlier pioneering explorers as like pushing a quill or a dagger into one's ear. The pain could be intense and even disabling. But if the diver continued down, at least the pain eventually disappeared when his stretched eardrums burst and the pressure differential was equalised.

There was a little bleeding from the ear perhaps, but nothing to speak of. The resulting deafness was often only temporary and the torn ear drums usually healed up again in a week or so. But if they failed to heal up, they remained perforated for the rest of the diver's life leaving him permanently deaf. Looking on the bright side, his ears never hurt again when he dived because now the air whistled freely through the holes in his eardrums without restriction. When he smoked his pipe, he could even blow smoke out through his ears to amuse his children.

Fortunately John noticed that the problem disappeared instantly if he swallowed or yawned, so he made a point of going through the motions of swallowing continuously during his descent. This was not so easy when his mouth had dried up with his initial anxiety.

Communications with the surface were extremely limited. Only the simplest of signals could be sent up or down by previously learnt, coded pulls on the signal rope. So the lowering and raising of the bell was a tricky operation. On top of all that, the water was uncomfortably cold. He put on many layers of clothing, which helped a little, but only a little.

John found the increasing darkness with the depth to be a little disturbing. It was even dangerous when there was a risk of the bell becoming entangled in unseen rigging or wreckage. So when the bottom was approaching he signalled for the bell to be lowered more slowly, in steps, in accordance with his rope signals. The view of the wreckage which he could see through the surface of the water in the bell was very limited. He was concerned that if the edge of the bell landed accidentally on a piece of wreckage as it was being lowered, it could tip over and flood, drowning him instantly.

And what about all those sea monsters that had bedevilled mariners through the ages? Superstitious seamen had dreamt up a host of terrifying monsters over the centuries. Now John was trespassing deep into their lairs. What was that shadow lurking behind the veil of darkness? What of the ghosts of all those poor drowned seamen that now haunted the tomb-like shipwreck? When he held his breath and left the bell, what was that prodding him from behind as he groped amongst the black slimy ribs of the mutilated wreck?

The experience of sinking into the inky darkness of the *Hindostan* on those first few dives would not have been for the faint hearted. The feeling of loneliness and isolation was almost unbearable. John seriously considered aborting his first dive on the wreck several times. He was very tempted to give the rapid pulls on the signal rope which meant "Emergency. Pull me up, fast!" But he gritted his teeth and held his nerve.

Neither was it a simple matter to clear away broken wreckage under water whilst working from the bell. John used various tools from his standing position in the bell, or, when he felt up to it, he took a deep breath, ducked under the edge of the bell and left its relative security for a short excursion. Whenever he did that, he tied himself to a rope attached to the bell so that he knew how to get back to it quickly when he was gasping for air.

The first few dives on the wreck were extremely difficult. It was just a tangled mess of unidentifiable blackened and broken timbers. At first he found it impossible to work out where he was on the wreck. But with each successive dive he gradually built up a picture of the ship's layout in his mind. He progressively cleared away the mass of tangled debris that barred his way into the ship's hold. Then he dug around in the silt and rubbish that had filled the hold to search for the valuable cargo. He had to feel his way through the black water. Razor-sharp barnacles that covered much of the wreck made numerous small cuts in his hands, which quickly became swollen and painful. But he persevered.

Despite all the hurdles, amazingly, they struck lucky. Over a long series of dives, they recovered no less than 3,000 silver dollars and no less than sixty tons of copper. Not only that, but the East India Company had agreed that they could keep whatever they recovered. They had obviously not expected the Bells to be so successful.

In winning their prize, the Bells and John Deane had learnt a very important lesson. Getting a pair of hands to work on the seabed had many advantages even if there were some limitations and dangers to using the diving bell. They could never have been so successful using just their poles. Our story might have ended there. The diving bell, despite its faults, was the answer everyone had been waiting for.

Or was it?

Serendipity was still in the game and about to play a trump card.

3
Breathing fire

John's parents had lived their entire lives in Deptford and he and his elder brother Charles had been born and brought up there. They lived in a small terraced house at 53 Hughes Fields. The busy river Thames flowed past the northern end of the road, just a hundred yards away. At the other end stands St Nicholas Church, which dates back to the seventeenth century, and where both John and Charles had been Christened. They were bordered on the west side by the sprawling Royal Deptford Dockyard and to the east by Barnard's private shipbuilding yard. Every business, for miles around, was either directly or indirectly associated with the sea and shipping.

Deptford is a large town next to Greenwich on the south side of the river Thames and it has a rich maritime history. It had developed into a major naval ship building area from the sixteenth century onwards and became the home of the first of the Royal Dockyards. Trinity House, the organisation responsible for the safety of navigation in British waters was formed there in 1514. Its first Master was Thomas Spert, then the captain of Henry VIII's ship, the *Mary Rose*. Francis Drake was knighted by Queen Elizabeth I on board his ship the *Golden Hind* at Deptford in 1581 and Peter the Great, Czar of Russia, came to Deptford in 1698 to learn about naval architecture, though he spent most of his time partying and upsetting his neighbours.

The roots of the Deane brothers run deep in this history. Their great great great grandfather was Sir Anthony Deane of Deptford who had been a close colleague of Samuel Pepys. Together they were responsible for rebuilding the British Navy during the reign of King Charles II, indeed Sir Anthony is known as the country's father of naval architecture. He had designed the sovereign's flagship HMS *Royal Charles*. He was the first to establish and record the structure of naval ships on scientific principles. He and Pepys were such close friends that they are both buried in the same church, St Olave's, Hart Street, in the City of London. Sir Anthony was closely related to General-at-Sea, Sir Richard Deane, who had previously not enjoyed such a constructive relationship with royalty having the dubious honour of being a regicide, and been a signatory to the Death Warrant of Charles I in 1648. Several of Sir Anthony's sixteen children became prominent seafarers and one in particular, named John Deane, followed in his father's footsteps in naval architecture. When

Peter the Great spent some time in Deptford, he and John Deane worked and socialised together, perhaps with a little emphasis on the latter. They got on so well that John Deane returned to Russia with the Czar and helped to rebuild the Russian navy.

Not a penny of the wealth or sign of any social standing of these previous generations reached down as far as John and Charles. Everything had been dispersed or lost in the intervening period. But because their father had spent his life as a seaman on East Indiamen, the boys had at least been entitled to the privilege of a three-year education in the nearby Royal Hospital School at Greenwich (now the National Maritime Museum). The school's stately buildings sit on the bank of the river Thames, just below the Greenwich Observatory perched on the top of the hill through which the international zero line of longitude was later established in 1884. The schooling provided a strict, tough, nautical education and made a big contribution to generations of the nation's sailors giving it the well-deserved reputation as "the cradle of the Navy".

A full size naval frigate named the *Fame* stood in all its splendour in the centre of the spacious grounds. It had been built on dry land from the 'waterline' up as a training ship for the education of the young students. They had to learn the name, function and construction of every part of the ship, not to mention all its ropes and sails. They were trained to climb all over the rigging including up the highest topmast.

When the boys graduated at the age of fourteen, they went straight to sea on a seven-year apprenticeship. The best of the bunch went into the Royal Navy or the East Indiamen. John had excelled at the school and he was rewarded with an excellent placement. He joined the East Indiaman *Warren Hastings* in 1813 having been bound out as the personal assistant to 'Fighting' Captain Tom Larkins for the next seven years. The ship had been originally built in the shipyard owned by Edward Barnard near his home and was one of eight East Indiamen he had built for the Larkins family.

Captain Larkins was an acknowledged hero from the Napoleonic War. Whilst in command of a previous *Warren Hastings* he had fought off a French frigate, the *Piemontaise*, for hours, even though his ship was hopelessly out-gunned. Only after his three masts had been shot away, his last gun was put out of action and his crew had been decimated did he surrender his ship. The story of Captain Tom Larkins's epic fight became a legend in his own time. By the time John joined the ship at Deptford, Napoleon had been defeated at Trafalgar by Nelson but he was yet to be finally conquered at Waterloo, two years hence.

As a young teenager, John was enthralled with the stories of the sea battles of the Napoleonic War. To have been able to work alongside a real-life hero like Fighting Tom Larkins was an enormous honour and inspiration for him. In many ways he regretted the fact that the seaborne war with France and Spain was over. He had missed his opportunity to launch into gallant fighting adventures on the seven seas. But John's experiences with Fighting Tom Larkins on his voyages to India and China nevertheless instilled in him a powerful sense of patriotism and a healthy appetite for adventure. Perhaps, one day, his turn would come.

Charles on the other hand, had not done so well at Greenwich and only managed to obtain an apprenticeship on a small coastal trading vessel, the *Ceres*. Charles was nothing like his younger brother. He was four years older, shorter, and of wiry build. He had been a sickly child, which had contributed to his poor performance at school. His outlook on life was generally pessimistic and he had few friends. He felt he was never given a fair crack of the whip and he was secretly jealous of his younger brother's ease at making friends and then his successful placement on a famous East Indiaman. He thought his younger brother was getting favoured treatment and the world was against him. But that didn't stop him from trying. For all his failings he did have a burning desire to succeed one day and to be a highly respected member of the community.

At the age of 23 years, John was still a bachelor and living with his parents in Deptford though he didn't spend much time there. Deptford was to where he returned, between his various expeditions. He wanted to travel and he found it difficult to settle down. Though his parents kept on at him to get a regular job like his brother, John felt there were too many opportunities for adventure out there. In between his travels, John had managed to court a pretty young lady named Agnes Norris whom he had known since childhood. She was the same age as John and the eldest of three daughters of William Norris, a long-standing friend of the family who owned a wharf on the Thames. In 1823 John and Agnes married in St Martin-in-the-Fields, a magnificent church which stands in the north-east corner of today's Trafalgar Square in London. It has strong naval connections and is the official Admiralty church. One of the many famous people buried there is Thomas Chippendale, the cabinet-maker, who had his workshop close by.

The young married couple were self-supporting, in a frugal way. John had saved some money from his East Indiaman voyages and had also made a small amount of money from his exploits with the Whitstable boatmen. But John still could not afford to buy his own house so they initially moved in with his parents in Deptford.

One day early in 1824, when there was a natural break in his offshore activities out of Whitstable, he returned home to spend some time with his young wife and parents. He was eager to relate his latest tales of treasure hunting and bell diving adventures.

At the time, Charles was employed as a ship caulker in the nearby private ship building yard owned by Edward Barnard. Caulking was a key skilled trade in ship-building. He had the job of sealing the gaps between the wood planks in a ship's hull and deck to make them watertight. To achieve this, he used a material called oakum which consisted of fibres of old rope, or old rope itself, soaked in molten tar. He drove the oakum in hard, between the planks using a special tool called a caulking iron. This is like a blunt chisel with a wide blade and when struck with a mallet, it forced the oakum deep into the gap. Finally he introduced molten pitch on top, which prevented the seawater from getting in contact with the rope and rotting it. The job was very important as the seaworthiness and longevity of the ship ultimately depended on it.

The caulker needed to have a small fire burning near him to melt the tar and to keep it in a molten state, so one of the greatest dangers, of which he was well aware, was that he might accidentally start a fire on board a ship. If that happened below deck, the ship would rapidly fill with toxic smoke and make it impossible for anyone to go below to fight the fire. Charles's training placed a great emphasis on avoiding such a potential catastrophe and the hazard was never far from his mind.

Barnard himself was a colourful and portly gentleman, having been born to a wealthy and successful family in Deptford who had been building ships on the Thames for generations. They had built more ships for the Royal Navy than any other private builder and that was on top of a string of East Indiamen for private clients. As a side-line, he was also one of the two Liberal MPs for the constituency of Greenwich.

But by 1824, the ship building industry was in recession in the aftermath of the Napoleonic War. Times were hard. The once-thriving yard was now relegated to just the repair and maintenance of East Indiamen, instead of building them. Barnard however, at forty-six years of age, was an eternal and increasingly eccentric optimist. As his ship building business dwindled, he spent more and more of his time enjoying the cut and thrust of politics. He had set up his political headquarters in the White Swan, a large public house which is still standing, just a short walk from his shipyard. Here he held court and lectured to his faithful constituents on burning political issues, whilst of course taking full advantage of the landlord's generous hospitality.

When John arrived back at his home in Deptford, there was much catching up to do with everybody's latest news. John knew that Charles was working in Barnard's shipyard so having settled back in, he strolled over to see how his brother was getting on. From the main gate he was directed to the dry dock where an old East Indiaman was undergoing a major refit.

He sensed immediately that something was wrong. He couldn't see anybody at work and he could smell something burning.

As he neared the dry dock he saw a small wooden building on fire. Dense smoke was billowing out of the open door. Edward Barnard himself was there, surrounded by a small entourage of workers. They were all anxiously looking at the burning building but strangely nobody was doing anything about it. More people arrived from all directions and the crowd grew bigger and bigger.

As John approached, he asked one of the workers if he had seen his brother Charles. The worker pointed with a trembling hand to the burning building. John was horrified. Nobody could survive for long in such a burning building. If the fire didn't get you, the poisonous smoke would certainly kill you. In an instant he ran instinctively towards the hut to rescue his brother. But he had only gone a few paces when he slid to an abrupt halt as he beheld a bizarre apparition.

What looked like a knight in shining armour suddenly appeared out of the smoke at the doorway. The figure paused nonchalantly in the doorway, apparently unconcerned with his perilous situation. Smoke billowed out all around him. Then he stepped out and strode majestically towards Barnard and the astonished crowd. What sort of super-human being could have survived inside the burning hut? How could he breath? One of the workers ran up to the knight and assisted him to take off his armoured helmet which was glistening in the sunlight. That was when John discovered the super-human knight was none other than his own brother. John was both relieved and flabbergasted.

He eagerly joined in with the workman to help Charles get out of what he called his *Smoke Dress*. John examined every piece of the equipment with delighted curiosity. A polished copper helmet with three windows was attached to a stout leather jacket. A pair of long leather trousers completed the outfit.

A leather hosepipe led away from the helmet to a wooden chest containing a bellows. Another worker had been pumping away, unnoticed, providing Charles with a continuous supply of fresh air all the time he had been in the smoke dress and inside the burning building. A second leather pipe dropped down from the helmet, alongside one of the trouser legs, opening at the level of the ankle. This was the exhaust or eduction pipe through which the pumped air escaped after circulating around the helmet.

Charles proudly explained that this was his newly invented smoke dress designed to allow a person to enter a burning building to put out a fire and save goods. He had arranged a small wood fire inside the hut to generate the smoke which he had then dutifully extinguished. It simulated the situation that might develop below deck in a burning ship. The whole exercise had been a demonstration of the equipment for the benefit of his employer, Edward Barnard.

John was mightily impressed. His brother Charles was about to make his fortune with a brilliant invention.

Barnard had encouraged Charles to pursue his invention and even helped to pay for the construction of the prototype equipment which he had been using for the demonstration. To help with its construction, Barnard had commissioned an up-and-coming Prussian immigrant engineer based in Soho, London to build the copper helmet to Charles's design.

That engineer's name was Augustus Siebe. He was a former artillery officer in the Prussian Army and had fought Napoleon's army at the Battle of the Nations at Leipzig in 1813 during Napoleon's ignominious retreat from Moscow. Both sides sustained heavy casualties during the battle, though Napoleon came off the worse and was obliged to continue his disastrous retreat to Paris. But one of the 50,000 casualties inflicted by the French was Augustus Siebe, however, his injuries had not been fatal and he had made a good recovery.

Later that year, Charles filed the specifications for his smoke dress invention. It was enrolled on 4th November 1824, Patent Number 4869. As a lowly ship caulker, Charles did not have the financial wherewithal to manufacture and supply such equipment but fortunately Barnard had offered to champion his cause and had generously sponsored him.

In fact, he did more than that. Within days of the successful enrolment of the patent, Barnard paid Charles the huge sum of £417 for an indenture of assignment of the patent. In today's money that would have been the equivalent of £30,000. So Barnard now owned all the rights to the patent for the next fourteen years. Part of the arrangement was that Charles maintained a personal interest in the invention and helped to promote the equipment. Barnard was quietly confident that he would be able to sell large numbers of the equipment to the fire brigades and the Admiralty.

The £417 was a huge sum of money for the young Charles Deane. He was in unusually high spirits when he returned to his home at 2 Charles Street, Deptford, that day. His wife Sophia was overjoyed and relieved with the boost to their struggling financial situation. They had three very young children, Charles, George and Harriett to feed and clothe and there was another already on the way. But Sophia secretly harboured misgivings that Charles and money might not be a good mix. He had never been any good at saving.

Be that as it may, Charles and Barnard worked closely together to promote the new smoke dress over the next few years. Their first call was to the Admiralty. The Admiralty could save vast amounts of property from fires with such equipment at their disposal. Charles wrote off to them in March 1825, offering to demonstrate the equipment. He was surprised and bitterly disappointed when his letter was returned with the scribbled note "Their Lordships will give him no further trouble". He couldn't understand it.

The London fire brigades were the next natural choice to whom to demonstrate the equipment. After protracted correspondence, the big opportunity came when they managed to persuade the prestigious and influential Society for the Prevention of Loss of Life by Fire in the City of London to view the dress and to listen to a presentation by Charles. John went along to help and they demonstrated the smoke dress to the public at the society's premises, 18 Aldermanbury, in the City in February 1829.

But nobody took the bait. Charles's presentation fell on deaf ears. The fire brigades could see no practical advantage in the smoke dress. Charles simply couldn't believe it. How could they *not* understand the usefulness of the smoke dress? He was so angry it almost drove him out of his mind.

This was all happening around the time the industrial revolution was rapidly gaining momentum. But progress did not come without its casualties. In the countryside, farmers were introducing machinery which replaced workmen and one of the greatest culprits was the new-fangled threshing machine. Its introduction was causing open rebellion amongst the farm labourers who were being put out of work and the issue was becoming a national problem. In Kent, the rebels had a mythical leader named "Captain Swing". Many fires were deliberately started by "incendiaries" in farms that had introduced a threshing machine and threatening notes were left behind signed by "Swing". Several properties were tragically lost along with horses and other valuable livestock. The public upheaval became known as the Swing Riots.

John Deane happened to be in Whitstable when one of these fires broke out in a nearby farm. Everyone in the neighbourhood, including John, ran to help put out the fire. There was pandemonium. Men and women formed human chains to transfer buckets of water from a pond to the fire. When John arrived, he found the stable was alight and filled with smoke. The horses trapped inside were kicking vainly at walls and doors and making terrible noises as they were tortured by the increasing smoke. Some men were frantically operating a small pump taking water from the pond and sending it along a long hose to the stable but the water jet was hopelessly inadequate. It looked as though the horses were doomed to be burnt alive.

John knew the farmer and his family quite well and he had dined there on many an occasion in the past. He also knew that there was an antique suit of armour inside the farmhouse. He ran in through the open door, snatched the helmet off the suit and ran to the pump operators. He disconnected the hose that went into the pond and told the men at the pump to carry on pumping air. He then picked up the other end of the hose and when the water stopped and air started to come through, he donned the helmet and stuffed the hose up inside it. Then to everyone's amazement, he strode into the blazing, smoke-filled stable.

After what seemed an age to the anxious crowd outside, one by one, John led the horses out, until all of them had been saved.

The farmer, with his family and the crowd of helpers cheered and congratulated him on his initiative and bravery. The farmer's wife collapsed in a flood of tears. They had feared the worst and what they thought of John's courageous deed was nothing short of miraculous. If the farmer had lost all his horses, he would have lost his farm. John had saved his family from destitution. Though John's make-shift equipment had been a rudimentary version of Charles's smoke helmet, it had worked effectively and clearly demonstrated it had a real practical application. The story of John's epic rescue spread all around Whitstable and his reputation as a local hero was firmly established.

Altogether, Barnard paid for five sets of the equipment to be built. One full set was deposited at the Gallery of the National Repository. But despite all their best efforts, not one set was sold.

The smoke helmet venture was dead in the water.

4
BREATHING WATER

John had become very familiar with Charles's smoke dress by the time he had helped him demonstrate it a few times. Within days of his demonstration in London he was back at sea, exercising the diving bell with his Whitstable friends. It was only a matter of time before the penny dropped and the similarity of the two activities dawned on him.

His brother's smoke dress went into a smoke-filled room with air being pumped to it. The bell went to the bottom of the sea with a supply of air being pumped down to it. In principle, they were both doing the same thing.

What would happen if he tried to go under water with the smoke dress? If the helmet could be made watertight, it should work. After all, the helmet would be acting just like a very small diving bell. It would be trapping a bubble of air around the diver's upper body and it had an infinite supply of fresh air being pumped down from the surface.

The smoke dress would simply become a diving dress and it would be far superior to a diving bell. The diver would be free to walk about, climb up and down and be totally mobile. He would no longer be trapped inside a bell with only very limited mobility outside it. He would have the sort of underwater mobility that previously had only been dreamt of. Perhaps it might not even be so wet and cold.

John did however appreciate it would not be all that simple. He knew that the way the smoke dress was designed and built it could never work under water. Many modifications needed to be made, but he decided the problems should not be insurmountable.

On his next trip home he went round to Charles's house and put his idea to him. Unfortunately Charles wouldn't hear of it and even ridiculed the suggestion. He belittled John just as he done all his life. He tried to make out that John didn't understand the business of an inventor and anyway he shouldn't try to muscle in on his invention.

As far as Charles was concerned the future of his brilliant smoke dress was with the Admiralty and the nation's fire brigades and certainly not with some hare-brained treasure hunting fantasy. And anyway, Barnard would never allow anyone to defile one of the few precious dresses, which he had bought and paid for at great personal expense. Charles was adamant and bluntly turned down John's suggestion.

John was feeling disappointed and bewildered as he walked

home, though he was determined to pursue his idea. He hardly slept a wink that night. All he could think of was how he should modify Charles's smoke dress to make it work under water. The next day he planned how he would make a second attempt to persuade Charles to let him adapt a smoke dress. He decided he would offer to pay all the costs himself because he knew that Charles was having great difficulty making ends meet then having five children and there was a sixth on the way.

In the evening, John went back to Charles's house and presented his carefully considered proposal. Charles had in fact been thinking about John's idea during the day and this time, though still quite sceptical, he was a little more receptive. After some discussion, Charles suggested that they should put the idea to Barnard and if he agreed, then perhaps it would be worth giving it a go.

Barnard turned out to be far more open minded than Charles. He listened with fascination to John's ideas and eagerly consented to him modifying one of the smoke dresses. Noticing Charles's reluctance, he encouraged him to help John as much as he could. Charles felt uncomfortable seeing John suddenly gaining popularity with his employer. It was the sort of thing that had happened to him all his life. Whenever John appeared on the scene, he would become the centre of attention and Charles would be sidelined. It just wasn't fair.

John lost no time. He collected a smoke dress from Barnard's yard and immediately set to work to make the helmet watertight. He used pitch to seal around the inside edges of the three windows and soldered up the rotating air valve opposite the wearer's mouth. He would await the results of their first diving trial before deciding what would need to be done next.

There were no pressing work requirements on Charles at the shipyard so the next day the two brothers loaded the equipment, including the heavy forge bellows, onto a handcart. They wheeled it half a mile along Five Bells Lane to the Croydon Canal, which ran north and south through Deptford. They came to a small bridge where the lane crossed the canal and decided it would provide a convenient location for their experiments.

Anyone wishing to visit the site today where the experimental dives took place, should be careful they don't get run over by a train. The

London to Brighton railway now runs along the course of the old canal and the New Cross Gate railway station stands over the actual trial site. The pattern was repeated all over the country. As the rail system took over from the canals for transporting freight, many of the railways were conveniently built over the redundant canals. Croydon Canal happened to be the nearest and least polluted water in the area where they could test the equipment. Swimming in the river Thames was not recommended. Indeed it was quite dangerous because of the high level of human waste with which it was grossly infected.

Having set up camp on the side of the canal, the two brothers went through a series of highly illuminating dives. Each time they entered the water, they discovered a new physical principle that impeded their progress and needed to be overcome.

John got dressed into the equipment for the first attempt. As soon as the helmet was lowered over his head he felt the same strange sensations as he had experienced during the smoke helmet demonstrations. If he spoke, his voice echoed loudly in his ears. The air rushing in by squirts from the bellows sounded particularly noisy. He could hear himself breathing and feel his heart pounding. Looking out through the three windows was quite peculiar. He thought it was like having his head inside a doll's house, and he was looking at the outside world through its tiny windows. Fortunately he didn't suffer from claustrophobia or he would have panicked immediately. In fact, it felt quite the opposite to John. It felt cosy and secure inside the helmet, a bit like living inside a doll's house.

Whilst Charles pumped away at the bellows, John stepped carefully into the canal. The water was only about six feet deep so there was no fear he would disappear forever. Nevertheless, he took it slowly. The cold water rose up his body but it thankfully stopped when it reached his chest. Then the jacket began to inflate like a balloon. It lifted him off the bottom and he wallowed about on the surface in a very undignified manner. Charles thought it was the funniest thing he had ever seen and he had never laughed so much in his life. It was all he could do to keep pumping to assure his brother of a supply of air.

Back to the drawing board. Or in this case, it was back to the shore.

John splashed his arms around like paddle wheels and finally got back to the canal bank. After a series of ungainly, acrobatic twists and turns, he found his feet and climbed back up the bank. For a moment he stood there, covered in black smelly mud, trying to work out what was so funny to Charles. When he had recovered his composure, Charles went over to John and helped take off the helmet and leather jacket. They sat down together on the bank, Charles still chuckling to himself and John, wet cold and muddy. John took some comfort from the fact that he had rarely seen his older brother laugh so freely. It was most unusual for Charles to show any sign of friendship to John.

By now they had gathered an audience of an elderly couple who had been strolling down the lane and stopped on the bridge to observe the strange antics in the water. Trying to ignore the inquisitive onlookers, John explained that the exhaust air will have to be released at the level of the upper chest or shoulders to prevent the jacket from inflating. He suggested that the best way to do that was by punching a large number of small holes in the breastplate or corselet of the helmet, front and back. That way, the air could escape freely without inflating the jacket. Charles was uncomfortable with the thought of such destructive modification of the smoke helmet but he was obliged to concede because Barnard had given his permission.

John also concluded that there was so much air trapped in the helmet and jacket that he needed extra weights to sink him. He thought that a few bags of lead shot should do the trick.

So John decided to call it a day and return home to carry out the necessary alterations. As they left, the grateful audience on the bridge waved their appreciation and walked on.

John went straight round to the workshops at Barnard's yard and punched as many holes as he could around the corselet, the bottom part of the helmet, until it resembled a sieve. He acquired a hundredweight of lead shot and some leather pouches and with the aid of his cart, transported everything back to his parent's house in Hughes Fields. Here John set to work filling each of the pouches with about fifteen pounds of shot. When he returned to the canal the next day, he was going to make absolutely sure he sank.

Early the following morning, the brothers loaded up the cart once more and pushed it to the canal. Charles decided it was his turn to try out the diving dress. John, being the younger and grateful for his brother's help, couldn't refuse. John slung four bags of lead shot over Charles's shoulders and tied them around his chest. He then manned the pump whilst Charles headed for the canal bank. The extra weight made walking to the water's edge a little awkward. If Charles fell over, with sixty pounds of lead tied around his chest he would not be able to get up again without help from John. Charles gingerly descended the canal bank, nearly slipping several times, and slowly made his way towards to the middle of the canal.

All went well. The cold water rose up his body as he waded into the deeper water and carried on rising alarmingly until it reached the level of his neck before it stopped. With the water level inside the helmet lapping around his chin, he made it to the middle of the canal and became almost completely submerged. At last, they were getting somewhere.

This time the jacket showed no signs of inflating and the exhaust air escaped freely through the many perforations in the corselet - problem solved. The only trouble was that as soon as his head had dipped below the surface he couldn't see a thing because he was now surrounded by a curtain of tiny bubbles.

He was just working out how they could overcome that particular problem when it happened.

From the bank John saw the helmet dip down and disappear from view. A moment later there was an eruption of bubbles followed by two kicking legs rising vertically up into the air. It would have looked hilarious to the uninitiated, but John realised that Charles's helmet would now be flooded and he would be drowned in seconds. He abandoned the pump, grabbed the air line and hauled it in as fast as he could. The pair of legs approached the bank and John leapt into the water. He grabbed the legs and dragged them to the bank. The body was a dead weight; Charles was wearing sixty pounds of lead and his helmet and jacket were full of water.

By now the legs had stopped kicking and gone quite limp. John summoned up all his strength and hauled Charles's upside-down body up the canal bank. Once on level ground he dropped the lifeless body, took out his knife and cut away the pouches of lead shot, slashed open the leather jacket and hauled off the water-filled helmet. Charles lay motionless, water dribbling from his mouth and nose.

John sat him up and shook him violently. Suddenly Charles coughed and vomited a stomach-full of canal water straight into his face. John carried on shaking and Charles slowly opened his eyes. He tried to talk, but that just made him cough and vomit again. Slowly, very slowly, Charles regained his senses. He muttered something unintelligible again. So John asked him to say it again. Eventually John understood him to be saying "More weights, more weights". John wiped his face and smiled with relief.

Thankfully this time there had not been an audience on the bridge to witness the accident and exacerbate their embarrassment.

Later that day, at his home, Charles, who was now more-or-less recovered from his ordeal was ready to help solve the day's latest problems. They agreed that the reason for the disastrous dive was the distribution of the weights. When Charles had tried to move forward he had stumbled on unseen debris on the bottom of the canal. His head had gone down and the air in the helmet and jacket had escaped. With sixty pounds of lead hung from his shoulders and no weights on his feet, Charles had landed head down, in a hopeless situation with no chance of recovering his position. His head was planted on the bottom of the canal and his buoyant legs were floating above him. If it had not been for John's prompt action he would most certainly have drowned.

He also remembered the problem with the bubbles obscuring his vision. John sympathised. The holes had to go. So he quickly set about heating up some lead shot and used them like soft rivets to plug every one of the holes he had so carefully punched into the corselet. He decided to revert to the leather exhaust tube but this time to cut it back so he could experiment with different levels for allowing the air to escape.

At the next visit to the site it was John's turn in the water. He had carefully repaired the slashed leather jacket, reinstated a shortened exhaust pipe and revised the weight distribution. As before, he was loaded up with four bags of lead shot, but this time they were hung from his waist. And to make absolutely sure he was not going to turn turtle in the water, he wore thick leather sandals fitted with heavy lead soles. He felt the arrangement was very cumbersome out of the water, especially walking with the lead-soled sandals. But once he was in the water the buoyancy of the helmet and jacket compensated for the weights and he could walk more easily.

John also made it to the middle of the canal. The top of his helmet was just breaking the surface. He saw the water level rise up the outside of helmet windows until he was looking through the yellow-brown water at the canal floor. He could see the weeds growing out of the mud. There were broken tree branches and all sorts of rubbish that had accumulated over many years. It was like a fairyland of mystical objects. He could even see small fish darting between the weeds. He was totally enraptured by the fascinating spectacle, his lively imagination filling in what he couldn't see. Perhaps there were bigger fish close by, or perhaps even valuables abandoned by robbers. Then he remembered why he was there. He began to experiment with raising and lowering the bubbling end of the shortened exhaust pipe. He found that the level of inflation and the level of the water inside the jacket moved up and down together corresponding with the level of the end of the pipe. If he lowered it, the jacket inflated and he became lighter. When raised, the jacket filled with water and he became heavier.

Another peculiar effect he noticed was that the level of the eduction pipe outlet affected his breathing. When it was lowest, near the level of his waist, air rushed into his lungs when he inhaled and there was a slight resistance to his exhaling. When he raised it to about the level of his chin he noticed a slight resistance to inhaling, but this time the air rushed out of his lungs when he exhaled. When he raised it any higher, the water level inside the helmet rose above his nose, so that was not a good idea. By trial and error, he found that the optimum position for the end of the pipe was about half way down his chest. In this position he felt no discomfort whatsoever with either inhaling or exhaling.

John noted one more concern, and this did worry him somewhat. If he leaned forward, the water level in the helmet again rose up towards his mouth and nose. He realised that if he leaned forward too far he would not be able to breathe at all. This confirmed to him how Charles's forward stumble could have had catastrophic consequences.

Whilst John was methodically conducting his experiments with the eduction pipe, he appeared to Charles to have stopped moving and he was getting a little worried. He had no way of knowing if his brother was alive or dead, but he kept pumping anyway. Eventually, John started to move about again and finally waded back to the side and out of the water, much to Charles's relief. But that quickly reverted to serious concern once more. John was mumbling, shaking and waving his arms about wildly. When the helmet and jacket eventually came off, all John could say was "It works, it works, it works!" He could hardly contain his enthusiasm.

John's idea to convert Charles's smoke helmet into a diving helmet had worked. It had involved his learning a few hard lessons about the physics of going underwater and redesigning the equipment. But by the time he had finished, John, with Charles's help of course, had invented the diving helmet.

The world population of helmet divers had begun and presently stood at two. Their next diving decision was a tough one. Where in the world to start?

5
Bombay or the Isle of Wight

As if on cue, the Honourable East India Company's ship *Carn Brea Castle* was wrecked on the south side of the Isle of Wight.

She had only just left Portsmouth, sailed east down the Solent and turned round the corner of the Isle of Wight to head west down the channel. The pilot who had been aboard to guide the ship out into open sea, had been transferred to his boat and had returned to Portsmouth. Then the *Carn Brea Castle* set a westerly course down the channel. She was fully laden with supplies for Bombay, India, including a large cargo of copper, all of which was insured at Lloyds for £100,000 (£7 million in today's money). Her passengers were mainly army officers and their wives. They were settling in to their cabins below, preparing themselves for a very long voyage. It was July and they were hoping for a warm summer's cruise down the channel.

The sailing ship was heading into the wind coming from the south-west so their progress was slow. She could not head directly into the wind and had to tack alternately to the left and to the right to make any progress. Then the wind suddenly freshened from the west. On turning to change direction on one of her tacks, the blustery wind snatched at the sails and the crew accidentally lost control of the ropes. The ship slowed down, refused to answer to the rudder and began to drift sideways inexorably towards the fatal shore. The crew fought desperately to regain control of the sails but just as the East Indiaman was approaching the precipitous cliffs on the south side of the Isle of Wight, she ground to a halt in rocky shallows. She was now completely at the mercy of the heavy seas, like a beaten boxer trapped against the ropes. The helpless ship lurched dangerously over onto her starboard side, all but capsizing. The huge breaking waves pounded her relentlessly. Her defenceless hull rolled about on the rocky seabed and inevitably became holed. The sea flooded in past the broken timbers filling her lower deck completely.

The voyage of the *Carn Brea Castle* was over before it had hardly begun.

But now if the ship broke up on the rocks, everybody on board was going to perish. They were surrounded by heavy surf. If they jumped into the sea they would be drowned or pulverised on the rocky shore. The demise of the ship had been observed from the shore and Preventive Service officers sailed out from the island. They made heroic efforts to save the passengers and crew and miraculously saved all except the ship's carpenter who had fallen into the water and drowned. The flooded lower deck actually helped the situation to some extent. It made the ship more stable because she now sat more heavily on the seabed and she didn't roll about so much with the waves.

The following day the high winds died down and the abandoned East Indiaman was left sitting upright in shallow water. Her hull had managed to survive relatively intact though it had been badly holed. Her hold was full of water even at low tide and the weakened hull was unlikely to survive another beating. There was only a limited window of opportunity to try to recover the ship's cargo before it would be scattered all over the seabed when the next gale finished the job and smashed the ship to pieces.

Back at Lloyds in London, the *Lutine* bell was solemnly rung to announce the ship's loss. Frenetic efforts were under way to arrange the salvage of the cargo. There was no time to lose. The Lloyds Agent at Whitstable was instructed to commission suitable salvagers and send them directly to the wreck. As it happened the Bells were away at sea but John Deane was there, staying with the Browning family. The Brownings were ship owners in the coastal trading business and John had been friends of the family for several years.

John had spent some time in Whitstable earlier in the year perfecting the diving dress, all at his own expense. He had built his own copper diving helmet which had two windows, was covered in leather to which a short leather jacket was attached. He had acquired his own forge bellows and modified it for diving by reinforcing the leather and making the pump handles longer to give more leverage and produce a little more pressure. With the help of his friends he had also been gaining valuable experience with the operation of the diving dress.

So when the Lloyds Agent broke the news of the loss of the *Carn Brea Castle* John immediately leapt at the opportunity. Thomas Browning, son of Matthew Browning Senior, helpfully offered himself and his boat for the project so the sloop *Albion* was quickly loaded up with John's diving equipment and supplies for the voyage. John sent a message to Charles in London to explain the situation and to meet him in Portsmouth, then he promptly set sail.

Charles was waiting in Portsmouth when the *Albion* sailed into the harbour. After a hurried briefing with the local Lloyds Agent they set sail once again and headed for the back of the Wight. At least there was not going to be any problem finding the wreck, she was sitting up conspicuously in the shallow water.

It was an ideal scenario for the Deanes to prove the usefulness of their diving equipment. The depth of the water inside the ship's hold was nominal, only about eight to ten feet at low water. They could operate from the deck above, which provided a stable platform to work from and there were no waves to contend with. They didn't even have to worry about tidal streams inside the shelter of the ship's hold. But everything depended on the weather remaining calm.

Fortune smiled on them. The weather stayed favourable and over the following two weeks John and Charles progressively emptied the hold of the stranded ship - to the great delight of the Lloyds underwriters. No sooner was the task completed than the weather suddenly deteriorated again and the wreck broke up. They had managed to recover the cargo in the nick of time.

The project could not have gone better for the Deanes. Charles was no longer a sceptic. He had been converted. He was at last convinced that John's modification of his smoke helmet into a diving helmet was a viable proposition.

That is, except for one thing.

When they had been diving while the tide was high, they had experienced great difficulty pumping the forge bellows to get air down to the diver. The extra ten feet of water depth, the difference between high and low water, was proving to be a bit of a challenge. It became physically very difficult to operate the pump and the men operating the pump tired very quickly. Extra men had been needed just so that they could take turns at the pump to keep the diver supplied with air.

If their diving helmet was ever going to be of serious use, they would need to be able to descend deeper than just twenty feet.

What they needed badly, was a better pump.

6
Rubber dresses

Diving Dress.

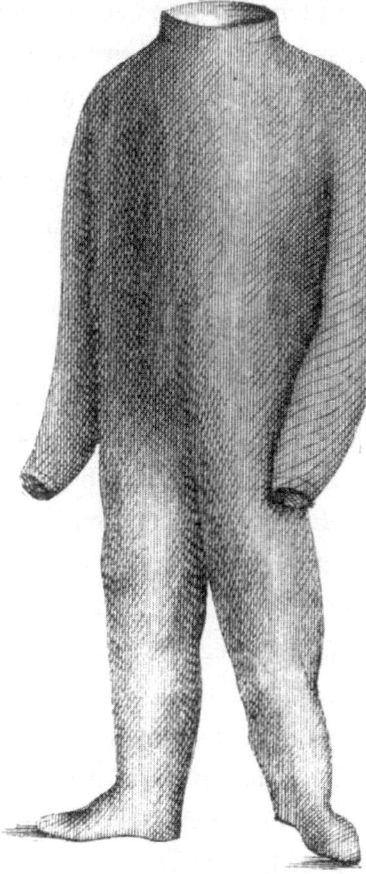

The natural place to go to get a better pump was back to Soho, and the manufactory of Augustus Siebe.

This is where Barnard had originally gone to get the smoke helmets produced. Siebe also had an excellent reputation as a pump manufacturer. He had invented a unique rotary water pump of his own design which had become one of his successful product lines. What is more, the Deanes had a pocket-full of money to spend, thanks to their successful salvage operation on the *Carn Brea Castle*.

Siebe accepted the challenge and built them a special three-cylinder, air pump. It was a superb piece of engineering. The pump was supplied in its own sturdy wooden case and it had two turning handles, one on each side and one of which was fitted with a large cast iron flywheel. It could develop the extraordinary pressure of forty-five pounds per square inch, which could force air down to a diver at a depth as great as one hundred feet. No such air pump had ever been built before.

In fact the pressure was so high that it could burst the hand-stitched leather hoses that the Deanes were using with their diving dress. So the Deanes discovered they now also needed replacement high pressure air hoses if they were to exploit the greater depth capability offered by the new pump. The trouble was, high pressure hoses hadn't been invented. Or so they initially thought.

By yet another amazing stroke of luck, serendipity played another trump.

A Scottish gentleman by the name of Charles Macintosh had recently invented a waterproof fabric that was both flexible and strong. The material consisted of two layers of cloth stuck together by a solution of Indian rubber dissolved in coal-tar naphtha. The revolutionary material opened the door to a vast range of unique products, from inflatable pillows and lifejackets to waterproof coats. The coats were by far the most popular of the entire range and quickly became known as "Macintoshes".

Another of Macintosh's popular lines was a new seamless hosepipe, which he sold to the London Fire Brigades. Originally invented by a William Baddeley in 1827, it was much stronger than the earlier stitched leather version. They had carefully tested the Macintosh hosepipe to evaluate exactly how much stronger it was. First they connected a leather hose, which had its end capped off, to a hand-driven water pump. They pumped and pumped until the pipe eventually burst, diligently noting the maximum pressure achieved. Next they connected a Macintosh hose and repeated the trial. Once again they pumped, and pumped ... and pumped.

The end point came with a bang, when the pump itself broke. The Macintosh rubber and canvas hosepipe was thus proclaimed the undisputed champion.

Macintosh had his main shop in what is today known as Trafalgar Square in London. It was just a fifteen-minute walk from Siebe's manufactory in Denmark Street. So roughly fifteen minutes after Siebe had described the Macintosh fabric to the Deanes, they were knocking at the door of Macintosh's shop.

Their discovery of Macintosh unexpectedly solved another problem that had been nagging the Deanes. The leather diving dress they had been using suffered terribly from repeated immersions in seawater. The leather deteriorated rapidly, it became stiff, brittle and leaked. The suits needed constant maintenance and repairs and replacing them was an expensive overhead. Macintosh was therefore commissioned to make them a one-piece waterproof diving dress. It turned out to be just what they wanted. It had integral feet, there were no stitched seams and the only openings were at the wrists and neck.

Before the diver donned his Macintosh suit, his wrists were first bound with bandages. When the suit was then put on, the cuffs were bound tightly over the bandaged wrists to make a watertight seal. The underlying bandages helped to protect the diver's wrists from the tight bindings. The material round the neck was gathered in and tied around loosely with a handkerchief. The helmet with its attached jacket was then put on. The arrangement was such that, as the diver submerged, the water level inside the helmet was kept lower than the open top of the diving suit gathered around the diver's neck. Consequently, the diver remained perfectly dry, and more importantly, warm. What luxury! Except that is, when the diver leaned too far out of the vertical, when the cold water would run over the top and into the dress. There was something especially unpleasant about the sensation of cold water running down one's neck and pooling around one's legs. But at least that could be avoided, most of the time.

At last, they were armed with professionally built, dedicated diving equipment. It was as perfect as it could be. The Deanes couldn't see how it could be possibly improved in any way. Theirs was the ultimate diving helmet and dress.

The Deanes were at last ready for their leap into deep water.

Surely fortune and fame were waiting just round the corner.

7
HMS Royal George visit

It would have been quite difficult deciding where to go next. The problem was there were just too many wrecks to choose from. They were spoilt for choice.

The most sensible way ahead was to pick a wreck that was known to hold something of value, was as shallow and sheltered as possible, and as near as possible to a convenient harbour.

Fortunately, when the Deanes had been in the Portsmouth area for the salvage of the *Carn Brea Castle* cargo, they had learnt of several wrecks, all of which fell into this category and were well known to the local inhabitants. John decided this should be his next port of call. He had in mind contacting a certain Henry Abbinett, a local ship owner who ran a public house called the Three Guns in Gosport. This is a small town on the western side of the entrance to Portsmouth harbour.

Abbinett was known to the Whitstable oyster fishermen because he also had his own oyster ground at the top of Portsmouth harbour. The owners of oyster fisheries around the country all tended to keep contact with each other for a very good reason. The oyster grounds were vulnerable to all sorts of biological attacks. Any one oyster bed could suffer a bad year, quite unpredictably. Whenever this happened, the grounds could be restocked with young oyster 'spat' from another oyster fishery in a different part of the country. The spat were extremely small, baby oysters that had attached themselves to gravel or stones on the seabed. That made them easy to dredge up and distribute elsewhere. In this way the failing oyster grounds could be re-seeded.

Another good reason for the communication between the various fisheries was that oysters which were not yet fully grown could be dredged up and transported to a new location which had a reputation for being better for fattening them up, and Whitstable had such a reputation.

This is how Henry Abbinett came to be known to the Whitstable oyster fishermen. So when John went to Portsmouth, he looked up Abbinett in nearby Gosport. The meeting went well. Abbinett, who was nearly ten years older than John, became very interested in the plans for diving the local wrecks, which were all in the relatively sheltered waters of the Solent, between the Isle of Wight and Portsmouth. Indeed, after Abbinett had seen John dive a few times he became so interested that he offered to buy John's obsolete diving helmet and dress. John saw no great problem with this. Abbinett was his friend and it made sense to John to have a friend who also dived. The sale would also help John with his finances, so a deal was struck.

The global population of helmet divers had leapt by fifty percent, from two to three.

John's simplistic view of life worked against him when he was surprised to find that Abbinett immediately set up in competition with him. Both he and Abbinett without each other's knowledge decided that to start with, the most convenient wreck to explore was that of HMS *Boyne*. She was a 98-gun three-decker that had accidentally caught fire whilst at anchor off Portsmouth in 1795. Her cannons had unfortunately been ready-loaded which meant that when the fire reached them, they fired off in all directions.

The *Boyne* had been anchored in the middle of a fleet when she caught fire. Several of the neighbouring ships had realised the impending danger and managed to weigh anchor and sail off to safety, but not all of them. A few ships stayed and were hit by the *Boyne's* unmanned cannon-fire. Three men were killed outright on the 100-gun, HMS *Queen Charlotte* when she was hit.

As the ship burnt, her rope anchor cable parted and she drifted with the slight breeze until she grounded near the shore at Southsea Castle, just half a mile from the entrance to the harbour. She eventually burnt to the waterline and the remains of her hull sank and settled into the soft seabed. Though on the north side of the channel leading into Portsmouth harbour, she remained a hazard to ships because some of her timbers came to within three feet of the surface at low water.

John invited Charles to join him in the exploration of the wreck. Charles had just moved his home from Deptford to the Old Kent Road, further into London where he thought he might stand a better chance of becoming a successful inventor. It was also more central and an easier place from where to travel to other parts of the country, such as Portsmouth. He readily accepted John's invitation as he needed to maintain his involvement with the developing opportunities with the diving helmet. So he packed his bag and jumped on the next available stagecoach to Portsmouth.

Their initial dives on the *Boyne* proved promising and they found many cannons and other salvable materials. The wreck was clearly well worth working on commercially.

But nobody could legally salvage anything from a naval wreck without first obtaining the permission of the Admiralty. Surprisingly, this was when John was beaten to the post. Abbinett wanted the wreck for himself and had got his application off to the Admiralty on 2nd May 1832 with an offer to remove the wreck. Not knowing about Abbinett's approach to the Admiralty, John sent his letter, also offering to remove the wreck at the end of the month, on 30th May. John had never anticipated that his friend Henry Abbinett would compete with him in this way. It was not the sort of thing that he would have done, had he been in Abbinett's place.

A period of confusion followed when both John and Abbinett assumed they each had the Admiralty's exclusive permission to work on the wreck. The Admiralty themselves had caused the confusion by mistakenly issuing instructions allowing both of them on the wreck.

By the end of July the Deanes had raised, amongst other things, two iron cannons, 2 cwt of copper sheet and stone shots. Interestingly they also brought up nineteen bottles of port and sherry, which turned out be eminently drinkable. Some of the bottles were distributed strategically amongst the Admiralty whilst curious visitors were treated to a small glass. Charles pointed out to the Admiralty that he had even allowed Mr M J Sweets, "a respectable tradesman of Portsea" and owner of the Wheatsheaf Tavern in Ordnance Row where Charles was lodging, to dive in his equipment to survey the wreck of the *Boyne*.

The global population of helmet divers was expanding steadily. It had now reached four.

Charles had also entered into correspondence with the Admiralty over the *Boyne* whilst confusion reigned over who had the rights to work on her. In his letter he had providentially included a request to be allowed to progress to working on the wreck of HMS *Royal George*, also sunk in the Solent. When the Admiralty finally got their act together, they issued clarifying instructions to Charles. The *Boyne* was to be the exclusive province of Abbinett, but he did have their permission to work on the wreck of the *Royal George*.

This was both good and bad news. Though they had lost the

Boyne they had gained the *Royal George*. But diving on the latter was not going to be as simple as it seemed.

The *Royal George* had been a proud, 108-gun ship and the sister ship of HMS *Victory*. She had foundered under mysterious circumstances whilst at anchor in the Solent in 1782. She took down with her the brave Richard Kempenfeldt, Rear-Admiral of the Blue and over nine hundred lives.

The ship had been careened over to starboard to carry out a simple repair job below the waterline on the port side of the hull. This was achieved by hauling the cannons on the port side towards the midline, so the change in the weight distribution caused the ship to tilt over to the starboard side. Whilst she was listed over, she suddenly filled with water and sank. Some people claimed her old hull had cracked open under the strain imposed by the careening. Others claimed that she had been careened over too far and water had rushed into open gun-ports on the low side of the ship. A court martial was held to establish the real cause of the sinking but it was heavily criticised for being a whitewash to cover up the fact that the hull was too old to have been in commission.

The tragedy remains the greatest ever loss of life from a shipping accident in British waters to this day.

The *Royal George* was one of the principal ships in the largest fleet ever assembled in British waters, consisting of about fifty warships and over three hundred merchant ships, all gathered at Spithead under the command of Admiral Lord Howe. They were preparing to sail to relieve the siege of Gibraltar. The "Rock" had been besieged by the French and Spanish for the past three years in an attempt to capture it whilst Britain was embroiled in the American War of Independence. The Franco-Spanish plan had been to capture Gibraltar and then to invade Britain.

The French and Spanish launched a final "grand assault" in September 1782 involving 40,000 men with 400 guns on land and 30,000 men with 200 heavy guns at sea. But even that failed. The attackers finally threw in the towel and the siege was lifted in February 1783.

The wreck of the *Royal George* lay in very deep water, some eighty to ninety feet. The shallowest point was her top deck in about fifty feet of water. To dive on this wreck involved a quantum leap in the complexity and risk of the diving operation. Apart from the engineering challenge to produce an air pump that could generate a sufficiently high pressure, which thankfully Siebe had overcome, they could not have known about the other dangers that awaited them as they pushed deeper and deeper. They were going to go deeper and for longer than anyone had ever been before.

Who could possibly know what might befall them?

The Deanes didn't have their own vessel so Thomas Browning of Whitstable came to their aid once more and sailed to Portsmouth to provide his sloop *Albion* for the diving operation. It did not take them long to find the wreck. Conveniently it was buoyed so that other ships could ensure they didn't foul their anchor in the wreck. It was going to take a lot of physical effort to work the air pump for Charles to be able to achieve the depth he wanted. So four men manned the pump, two on each side. John held on to Charles's air hose and a rope lifeline tied around his waist as Charles stepped off the side of the boat onto a ladder, which led down to the wreck.

This ladder was *sixty feet* long! Where on the small sailing boat could *that* have come from?

The ladder trail leads back to Great Yarmouth. That is where John had met a certain Captain George Manby, a controversial and prolific inventor credited with the invention of the mortar-fired rescue line used to establish a line with a shipwreck near the shore.

But more to the point, Manby had invented a *sectional* ladder. It was originally designed to be able to be extended out over ice to help rescue people who had fallen through and were in danger of drowning. It was an excellent idea but not a commercial success. So when Manby had seen one of John's diving operations on the wreck of the *Guernsey Lily* near his home town of Great Yarmouth earlier that same year, he had lent him the ladder to try out as a means of getting to and from the seabed. The Deanes used the ladder successfully for their initial *Royal George* operations but later dispensed with it in favour of a weighted rope ladder.

As Charles slowly descended the ladder down to the *Royal George*, the men on the air pump initially found it very easy to turn the handles. But as Charles passed twenty feet, then thirty feet, the resistance on the pump steadily got greater and greater. By the time Charles landed on the deck of the *Royal George*, all four men were straining to keep the handles turning. John was hoping and praying the new air hose didn't burst with the unusually high pressure inside. He was also becoming concerned at the unexpected high temperature of the air being delivered by the pump. He could hardly touch the brass fitting at the pump where the air came out, it was so hot. What was making it so hot? Would it catch fire?

As Charles had descended the ladder, one rung at a time, his concern grew as it got darker and darker until he could hardly see his hands in front of his helmet. His anxiety rose until he could feel his heart pounding in his chest. He stopped several times, frozen with fear. Each time he summoned up a little more courage and took a few more steps further into the blackness. Fifty feet down, his feet eventually landed on what he presumed was the deck as he couldn't see a thing in the total darkness. He gave a single pull on his lifeline to signal he had reached the bottom. Without letting go of the ladder, he pressed his face hard against the window of the helmet and strained his eyes. He dare not make a move because he didn't know what was beneath him, or around him. He could easily fall off the wreck or into a hole and drown. Minutes passed. Very slowly, his eyes became more accustomed to the darkness and he was able to make out the ladder in front of him and then a vague silhouette of the wreck around him. He dared to look down in front of him. At last he could faintly see the sloping deck he was standing on. There was silt and debris everywhere. Broken timbers lay chaotically all about. Dark holes in the decking threatened to swallow him up.

This was just the sort of place for nine hundred ghosts to haunt. No doubt the ghost of Admiral Kempenfelt was right behind him, watching his every move.

As more minutes passed by, Charles began to see a little more clearly. He was now able to make out that he was near the bow of the ship. He could see the silhouette of the broken bowsprit disappearing into the gloom. On his left, the side of the hull disappeared down into total blackness.

John had previously lashed a coiled rope to the bottom of the ladder, which Charles now untied. With one end securely tied to the ladder, and holding the coiled rope tightly in his hand, he stepped gingerly over towards the bowsprit. He had to hold on to pieces of timber to steady himself and prevent himself from sliding or tripping over. Their surfaces were smooth, slimy and entirely unpleasant to the touch. Everything he touched released plumes of black clouds that further hindered his vision. If he waited a moment, the slight current carried the black clouds away and he was able to see again.

He climbed up to the bowsprit and saw that it had been broken off near its base where a large brass reinforcing ring, about four feet in diameter, was still loosely attached. This was exactly what Charles wanted to see, large pieces of brass. This is where there was money to be made. He tied the rope off on the brass ring and followed the rope about thirty feet back to the ladder. He'd had enough. He pulled on his lifeline to signal to John that he was about to come up.

As he climbed the ladder it came as a sweet relief to see the darkness give way to a deep green light. This became brighter and brighter until his helmet broke through the surface. The bright daylight was blinding. He blinked and screwed his eyes up so he could see enough to climb back on board the boat. As soon as he was on board, John helped him off with his helmet and jacket. He could hardly contain himself and poured out questions about what was it like? What had he seen? What was down there?

Charles was exhausted. He had been down about half an hour but it had felt like only five minutes. When he got his breath back, his descriptions of his adventure gushed out. It had been a scary but fantastic experience. What was more, he had found a heavy brass ring at the bowsprit, which he thought could be easily recovered. So they decided that John should go down next and attach a strong lifting rope to recover the ring.

John couldn't wait to get kitted up. They needed to be fairly quick because the slack water between the tides would only last another fifteen minutes or so. John climbed into the Macintosh suit only to discover it was cold and wet. Charles had leaned over a little too far during his dive and water had run over the neck opening and into the suit. But there was no time to lose so he just got on with it. The men at the pump got back to work. Charles tended John's air hose and lifeline whilst Thomas

Browning paid out the thick rope that John was to tie onto the brass ring. John got on the ladder and purposefully climbed down.

He descended without any hesitation. He had dived in black water many times before, though this was the first time he had been down so deep. The main difference he noticed was the increasing pitch of the hissing sound of the air entering the helmet with each stroke of the pump pistons. It reminded him of his bell dives on the *Hindostan*. But this time he was not so cold and free to move about as he wished. It all felt quite natural to him. John was in his element.

On the bottom he signalled on his lifeline that he had arrived. After a brief pause whilst he waited for his eyes to become acclimatised to the darkness, he grabbed the rope tied to the bottom of the ladder and followed it along to the bowsprit, hauling the heavy lifting rope along with him. The previous experience he had gained on the *Hindostan* stood him in good stead. The conditions on the two wrecks were quite similar so it had been useful training for him. Without wasting a moment of time, he ran the lifting rope through the brass ring twice and tied it off securely. The round turn and two half hitches was a classic seaman's knot, very secure and he could do it blindfold. He untied the line that Charles had run out from the ladder, today it would be called a distance line, and made his way back to the ladder.

After signalling that he was about to come up, he confidently climbed back towards the surface. As he ascended, the pressure around him dropped and the air in his helmet expanded, bubbling out freely all around the bottom. As he neared the surface the bubbles were rushing up in front of his helmet in such profusion, he could hardly see. They reflected the sun's rays as they danced upwards and John was dazzled by a magnificent visual display of effervescent flashing lights all around him. He stopped for a moment to enjoy the spectacle and then climbed up and stepped aboard the boat.

Charles was secretly surprised at the speed with which John appeared to have accomplished his task. It had looked a fairly difficult job to him. Maybe John had not been entirely honest and he was covering something up. Maybe he never even made it to the bottom, after all, he almost gave up himself. There was one way to find out. That would be when they pulled on the lifting rope. Charles bided his time patiently. He would soon know.

They got John out of the helmet and suit as quickly as they could. The exhausted men on the pump were delighted and relieved that their strenuous labours were over for the day. Next the anchor was raised and the boat drifted a little way until it was brought to a halt by the taught lifting rope. Charles then had to accept reluctantly that John had completed his diving task quickly and efficiently. It did not come easily to him to acknowledge that his younger brother was better than him at anything. But it happened with annoying regularity. The lifting rope was transferred to the boat's anchor winch and then they waited. The tide was due to start running towards the west and when that happened, John had calculated that the boat would drag the brass ring off the broken stub end of the bowsprit.

Slowly the tide picked up. The tension in the rope which was run over the bow increased. But nothing happened. The tide picked up a little more and the rope started to creek and strain. Then the bow of the boat began to dip down. What if the brass ring didn't pull off? The boat might be pulled under the water as the tide rose! The bow dipped further and further. John became seriously worried. When it began to look as though the boat was in danger of sinking he got an axe from Thomas Browning and made his way up to the bow. If the bow dipped a few inches more he was going to cut the rope.

The time came. The bow was now dipping dangerously close to the surface of the water and John raised the axe. Suddenly, the boat shuddered from stem to stern and the bow leapt up. The axe went flying into the air and John was nearly thrown over-board but he managed to grab some rigging just in time.

Something had definitely given.

By the way the boat's bow went back down again and remained fairly low in the water, John guessed that there was a heavy weight suspended from the end of the rope. Two of the crew went to work on the anchor winch and slowly but surely hauled the huge brass ring up until it was just breaking surface and bouncing against the bow of the boat and gouging into the woodwork. It must have weighed a quarter of a ton. No wonder the boat's bow was low in the water.

They had at last recovered a very valuable piece of metal,

which they knew would help them recoup their expenses. It was also real evidence of the usefulness of the novel diving helmet and dress. They sailed back into Portsmouth harbour happily but with a little difficulty. The boat's rudder was almost out of the water and the large object under the bow did nothing for the steering. But the effort was worth it.

John was now bursting with confidence and full of optimism for future diving operations. He couldn't wait to get back down to the *Royal George* and explore the magnificent ship. It was a time capsule. The ship had been frozen in the time of the French wars and he was one of the first people to visit the ship since it sank some sixty years previously. He chatted away with Thomas Browning like a child on the eve of all his Christmases rolled into one. Charles on the other hand was sitting quietly on the deck, on his own. He was staring at the sea, deep in thought and appeared a little unhappy. He had found that his dive had been a little too scary for him. As a child he had never liked the dark and his experience in the blackness underwater brought back terrifying memories of his childhood nightmares. He couldn't understand how John could have been so happy down there.

The Deanes' successful dives on the *Royal George* attracted the attention of Captain Basil Hall RN, a retired Scottish naval officer of Portsmouth noted for his adventurous travels, scientific interests and writings. Being a regular contributor to the *Nautical Magazine*, he wrote a description of the Deanes' activities in 1832. The article included a rare and valuable illustration of the diving helmet. This version sported a short flexible tube tied to the side of the helmet. This was the eduction tube which was an early arrangement for exhausting the air from the helmet but it was not incorporated in later models. In use, the tube would have been attached to the front of the diver's chest to allow the exhaust air to vent at that level.

Despite this clear interest in the diving equipment at a senior Royal Navy level in Portsmouth, it failed to make any progress up the naval chain of command. The Admiralty nut was proving difficult to crack.

By now the Deanes knew that they had invented a uniquely useful piece of equipment that would revolutionise underwater work. They realised that their lives were going to be changed forever, even if it was taking a little longer than they had hoped. John, in particular, had decided that he would pursue a full-time diving career, whilst Charles was hesitant. He could see that John had a natural aptitude to diving whilst he himself was never really comfortable under the water, especially when it was deep and dark. That was when he had to force himself to carry on with the dive. The darkness frightened him. His imagination ran riot and his mind played tricks, conjuring up all sorts of threatening monsters and ghosts that had followed him around since childhood.

There were several goals they could now set themselves. Wealth was an obvious one. But another one was personal recognition. The ways in which each of the two brothers responded to their new goals were to be in stark contrast to each other.

The problem was that Charles considered the diving helmet was *his* invention. *He* was the one who had designed the smoke helmet. It was *his* name on the smoke helmet patent. It was one of *his* helmets that had been used to test out the diving application. The diving helmet was simply *his* smoke helmet being used under water, rather than in a room filled with smoke.

Charles saw the diving helmet as *his* long-awaited opportunity for personal recognition. It was everything he had always wanted. In Charles's mixed up mind, his younger brother John had little or nothing to do with it. It was only a matter of time before Charles's distorted view of the truth broke through to the surface.

There was a time bomb hidden in the plot, and it was ticking.

Part Two
Struggle and Strife

8
Blind eyes, deaf ears

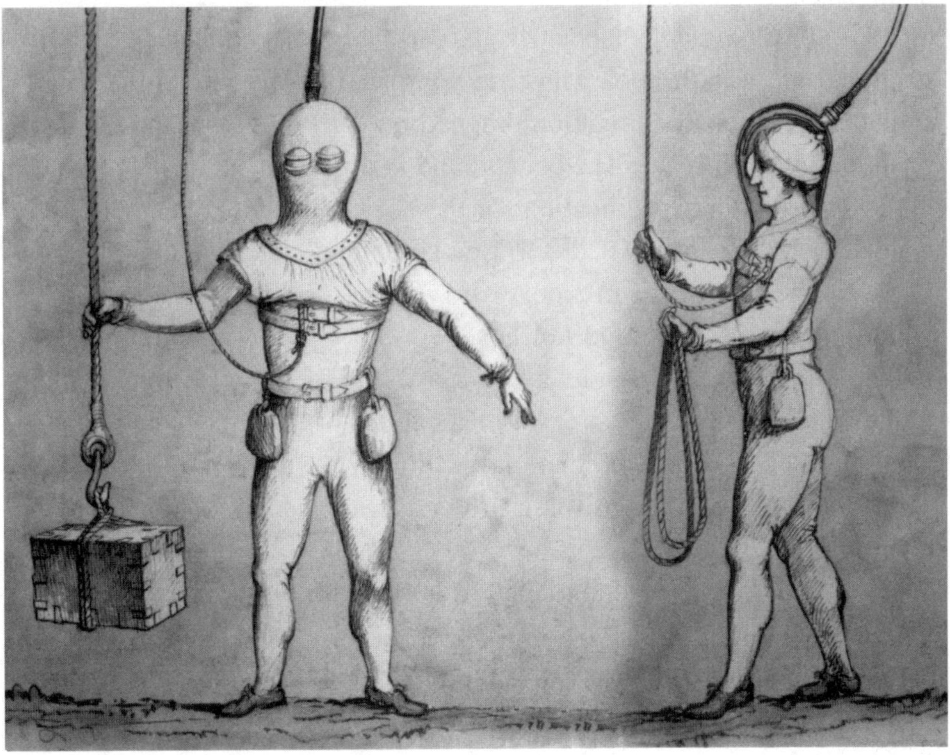

Charles's assumption that his smoke helmet patent also protected John's diving helmet conversion started to unravel when a salvage diver named John Parker Marsh entered the picture.

Marsh had been using a small diving bell to carry out salvage activities until 1829, but having seen John Deane in action with his new diving helmet, he commissioned him to assist on a couple of his wreck contracts. John gave a convincing performance and it so impressed Marsh that he decided to build his own set of helmet diving equipment in secret.

But somebody spotted what was going on and the news soon reached John, who passed it on to Charles who immediately blew his top! His patent rights were being infringed! Charles went straight to Barnard in Deptford. Marsh had to be stopped from copying the patent at all costs.

The inevitable happened. Barnard, whose ego matched both his girth and his wealth, took Marsh to court in 1831 to defend the patent rights. The expensive litigation dragged on for two years, and Barnard eventually lost his case. The court found that Charles had not made any claim in his patent specification for the use of his smoke helmet under water. He had clearly called it a "smoke helmet" because his intention was specifically to use in smoke. It was not designed to work under water and his design could not have worked under water. Charles had not intended or even considered the possibility of using his smoke dress under water. His patent was for "An apparatus or machine to be worn by persons entering rooms or other places filled with smoke or other vapour, for the purpose of extinguishing fire or extricating persons or property therein".

If there was no claim, there was no protection. The law was that simple.

Charles was furious with the court's finding. It drove him mad! In *his* mind, the court must have got it wrong. As far as he was concerned, the diving helmet was still *his* invention. And that was that.

If truth be told, the smoke dress as built to Charles's specification could not have been used under water in any case. It just would not have worked. John had had to make fundamental changes in its design and construction to make it work under water, as they had discovered during their entertaining trials in the Croydon Canal.

Whilst all this was going on in the background, the Deanes embarked on a campaign to convince the Royal Navy that the diving helmet was a useful tool to have at their disposal. They had decided that this was the best way forward to gain recognition and acknowledgment for their invention, not to mention reward.

All Royal Navy ships would benefit from underwater inspection, cleaning, repair and maintenance. All those lost anchors and cables could be recovered, as well as all the valuable items accidentally lost or even deliberately ditched overboard. Government property could be salvaged from lost ships and sunken ships could be raised. The potential value of the diving helmet to the Navy was obvious for all to see.

All except the Admiralty, that is.

The Deanes went to Portsmouth in 1831 specifically to demonstrate their equipment to the Navy. Charles got John to dive at the entrance to the basin in Portsmouth Dockyard. The demonstration was observed by, amongst many others, the Chief Mechanist for the Navy, Simon Goodrich. He was a remarkable man. He had a wide remit and was responsible for establishing many of the Navy's engineering facilities in Portsmouth Dockyard. He worked closely with Sir Marc Isambard Brunel and had set up the Portsmouth Block Mills. In 1831 he was nearing the end of his productive career and was just about to retire when he met John and Charles.

Goodrich certainly considered the diving equipment held great potential for the Navy. He even produced one of his many detailed pen and ink drawings for which he was famous. It showed a two-windowed helmet attached to a short, sleeveless jacket that came just halfway down the diver's chest. The diver wore a woolly hat under the helmet. Two weighted pouches hung from the waist and he wore weighted shoes. The diver was dressed in a one-piece waterproof suit that extended up inside the helmet. An air hose led from the helmet up to a reciprocating air pump with a flywheel, placed in a boat at the surface.

Goodrich's drawing also helps to clarify the derivation of the diver's red woolly hat. How this iconic item of a helmet diver's clothing became established has always been a bit of a controversy. There are several conflicting accounts. The Goodrich sketch dispels all the other claims as it shows the diver distinctly wearing a woolly hat. It was a necessary part of the clothing simply to help keep the diver's head warm because of the very cold air that flushed around inside the helmet. At that time, a red woolly hat was a common form of headdress worn by sailors, so it was the natural contender for thermal protection inside the chilly helmet.

Despite the clear demonstration of the effectiveness of the diving helmet on the Navy's doorstep at Portsmouth, the eyes of the Admiralty glazed over once more and they showed no further interest.

Disappointed with the Admiralty, the Deanes next appealed to the public.

They carried out a series of demonstration dives over a period of five days in January 1832. The location they chose was near the steps leading down to the river Thames in front of the Royal Hospital at Greenwich, their old school. It was a theatrical setting. Charles, wielding his seniority over John, invited "the Nobility, Gentry, and inhabitants of Blackheath, Greenwich, Deptford and their vicinities" to see him descend from a vessel and walk around the bottom of the Thames at low water. He made no charge for the demonstration, but he did invite those "Ladies and Gentlemen who may be pleased to contribute their Patronage and Support" to leave any donations with Mr Mattison of the Old George Tavern at Greenwich. That tavern today is called the Trafalgar Tavern and is well worth a visit.

Ominously, Charles made no mention of his younger brother John. On the contrary, he referred to himself as "*the inventor*" having "invented, at very great expense". It was becoming increasingly obvious that he had no intention of sharing any credit with John and every intention of claiming the diving helmet idea as his own. John simply put it down to his brother's eccentric behaviour. It wasn't that important to him and if it kept his brother happy, he could see no great harm in it.

The Deanes tried to convince the Navy yet again. This time, in 1832, they went to the newly built Sheerness Dockyard on the Isle of Sheppey in the Thames estuary. Sir James Beresford himself was there to see the demonstration. Flag-Lieutenant Washington from HMS *Ocean* volunteered to try out the equipment. His dive went without a hitch and he himself was delighted with the experience. Indeed everyone was quite pleased, but once again despite the local enthusiasm the Admiralty yawned and paid no further attention. Letters from the Deanes to the Admiralty offering the invention for their use were politely and consistently returned with their standard rejection, "Their Lordships will not interfere".

Things just weren't going as well as they should have. The patent protection had been successfully challenged and the Admiralty were not exactly overwhelmed with the concept. It looked as though it was going to take the Deanes much longer than they had expected to exploit the diving helmet commercially through sales to the government.

So how could the Deane brothers cash in on their novel equipment?

If nobody else was interested, the only hope they had of turning the diving helmet to their advantage, was by using it themselves.

9
TREASURE ISLAND

In 1828, John and his young wife Agnes had moved out of the family home in Deptford and settled in Ramsgate. It was a small terraced house at 6 Liverpool Place where they lived for the next six years and where their first three children, Edmund, Henry and Agnes, were born. The pretty terrace is still there today, though renamed Liverpool Lawn. From the end of their road they had a magnificent view from the cliff-top looking down over the picturesque harbour and out over the moody North Sea.

Ramsgate was a strategically important location for John, being on the eastern-most tip of Kent. From there he could sail westwards to Whitstable and up the Thames estuary to London, or north up the east coast of England, or south and west into the English Channel.

William Bell of Whitstable had temporarily teamed up with John and lodged at the house with John's family. With his assistance, and crucially his boat the *Perseverance*, John was able to begin diving independently of Charles. Charles was reluctant to commit his life to diving fulltime. John's decision to go-it-alone is hardly surprising bearing in mind Charles's relative inaccessibility, his egocentric attitude and his bizarre claims to have been the sole inventor of the diving helmet and dress. Charles missed a golden opportunity when his egotistical attitude progressively forced John to dive separately. John would have made him an indispensable and loyal diving partner if Charles had only given him the chance. But that was not how Charles saw the world.

The brief William Bell and John Deane partnership proved to be quite productive. William was the eldest and most experienced of the Bell diving brothers and being seven years older than John he had a lot to teach him. They struck lucky when they found the wreck of the Ordnance Transport Ship *Guernsey Lily* which had foundered off Great Yarmouth in 1799. She had been carrying twenty five bronze field guns so she offered excellent salvage prospects. The project progressed so well that George Bell came and joined in the operations. They recovered several cannons which were so perfectly preserved that John fired a royal salute from the *Perseverance* off Great Yarmouth on 8 September to commemorate the Coronation.

The local papers were delighted with the novel diving activities on their doorstep and their reporters eagerly followed each day's events.

The curiosity of the reporters at one stage was a little intrusive and John became a little frustrated with their interference. This resulted in his sense of humour getting the better of him and when an inquisitive reporter asked why he carried such an enormous quantity of lead weights when he dived, John replied that it was to compensate for the phenomenon that his strength was markedly increased when was under the water. In fact he could easily bend the ends together of a large iron crow bar, all of which was faithfully reported in the following day's newspaper.

By 1833, John had established a solid professional relationship with William Edwards, a prominent ship owner and skipper from Whitstable. William was the strong silent type though he knew exactly how to keep a rough ship's crew in order. He could turn his hand to just about anything and he got on with things. He had inexhaustible patience and never made a fuss. His wife was an energetic and supportive lady and together with their young daughter they all lived in a large house a short walk from the harbour.

John and William were at the beginning of a life-long business partnership. However, for their first, speculative ventures, and ultimately for their long-term success, both John and William needed additional financial support. In particular, they needed progressively larger boats as their diving business expanded and they operated further afield. Their salvage operations were notoriously risky and required funding for long periods of time before a return could be expected. They therefore took on two silent partners in their ship-owning ventures.

One of these was Philpot Wood. He was a shipping agent who assumed the important mantle of Lloyds Agent in Whitstable in 1833. John could not have asked for a more useful man as a partner than the Lloyds Agent. Apart from the all-important financial support, with Philpot Wood on board John had direct access to privileged intelligence on shipwrecks and salvage opportunities. Wood was well educated and a successful businessman so he was also a helpful advisor in business matters whenever John needed it.

The other partner was Dr James Williams, the principal and highly respected medical doctor serving the Whitstable community. Dr Williams knew just about everybody in the town and he was a very popular figure. John wisely surrounded himself with some of the most accomplished and creditable characters in Whitstable. He built himself a team that had the best possible prospects of long-term success.

Charles on the other hand, was a committed loner. He had exploited his four years seniority over John to the full and drawn heavily on his support, as well as that of John's associates. Sadly, when it came to showing gratitude or sharing credit, Charles was not the most generous of men. He had taken full advantage of John's youthful loyalty to obtain the essential support for his diving projects.

Though the time was ripe for a major diving project, they were going through a quiet patch and they seemed to be running out of steam. They badly needed direction.

Then John heard about the wreck of the *Enterprise* through the Whitstable grapevine.

It was just an obscure rumour which reached Whitstable from Belfast, Ireland in 1833. One of the Preventive Service men employed in Belfast was a native of Whitstable and during his tour of duty he had heard a local tale of a treasure-laden slave ship that had been wrecked on an uninhabited island a little way along the coast, many years ago. The island in question was desolate Mew Island, one of a small group known as the Copeland Islands. The ship had been on the final leg of its three-leg voyage, popularly referred to as the Slave Triangle.

During the slave trading period, a ship would leave Liverpool with English goods to sell in West Africa, where, after disposing of its Liverpool cargo, it would take on board a cargo of slaves for America. After delivery of the unfortunate slaves the ship would return to Liverpool with the proceeds of the sales and a cargo of sugar and fruit from Havana for sale back in Britain. The lucrative triangular voyage was thus completed. Liverpool had been the principal British port involved in this miserable trade since its outset.

One of these slave ships had been the Liverpool-owned *Enterprise*.

The *Enterprise's* proceeds from the sale of its 363 slaves and other cargo were said to be an incredible £200,000 (about £14m in today's money). So the barrels of silver dollars were stacked high in the hold of the *Enterprise* as she headed back to Liverpool across the Atlantic in 1803. Her master, Captain John Heron, would have been looking forward to an early retirement as a wealthy man.

But that was before the storm.

With just about a hundred miles to go, only one more day before reaching Liverpool, the *Enterprise* was suddenly caught in a fierce gale. The helpless ship was blown a long way off course and she ended up crashing into the rocky shore of Mew Island. She went to pieces within minutes of striking and eleven of the crew were either drowned or smashed to pulp on the rocks. It was amazing that any of them survived at all. The precious load of silver dollars went to the bottom and scattered themselves amongst the rocky crevices.

When the storm was over, there was very little sign left of the ship, just floating wreckage and mutilated bodies. Hoards of seagulls noisily gorged themselves on the fresh meat. The *Enterprise* had taken her treasure to the bottom of the sea. Obscure Mew Island had now been promoted to a veritable treasure island. However, the treasure had not been conveniently buried in chests in a hole on the beach, or stacked neatly in a cave by obliging pirates. It was dispersed untidily over a wide area of the seabed. The heavy silver coins rolled into crevices between the rocks and readily buried themselves under the sand, disappearing from sight.

A Mr Haughton was sent from Liverpool to attempt some sort of salvage, and though he did manage to recover a few silver dollars using tongs on the ends of poles, the vast majority of the silver remained hidden on the seabed.

Thirty years later, the tale of the treasure on Mew Island had all but melted into obscurity. But when the whisper of the treasure reached John's ears it sounded like an exciting venture, though he realised he would be taking a huge chance. The stakes were high, but the jackpot could be enormous. John decided to accept the challenge despite the unfavourable odds. The speculative treasure hunting expedition would involve a fifteen-hundred-mile round trip across unpredictable seas. So John mitigated the risk as best he could by arranging to visit several known wrecks on his way round the coast.

John and William Edwards embarked on their voyage later than they would have liked in 1833. It was already October. The season was fast drawing to an end, the nights were drawing in and they were pushing their luck. Their plan optimistically included a visit to the Scilly Isles where John had obtained the permission of the Admiralty to attempt to raise the cannons lost with HMS *Colossus*.

The *Colossus* was one of Nelson's veteran warships. The 74-gun 3rd-rate had run on to the treacherous rocks near St Mary's Roads on her return journey from the Mediterranean in 1798. She took with her to the bottom a priceless collection of 2500-year-old Greek vases owned by Sir William Hamilton, Britain's envoy to the Royal Court at Naples. The fame of the vases had been further enhanced when examples had been used as props in revealing paintings of the voluptuous and scantily dressed Lady Emma Hamilton, Sir William's wife and Nelson's mistress.

After an uneventful passage to the Scilly Isles, John searched for and quickly found the wreck of the *Colossus*. He successfully raised several iron cannons and brought them ashore at St Mary's. On examination, they turned out to have been charged with gunpowder intended to be fired as distress signals before the ship had gone down.

A local man, Master Gunner Ross inspected the guns and made a surprise discovery. He found that when he struck one of the cannons with a hammer, it actually fired, even though it had been under water for thirty-five years. The wadding landed on nearby Rat Island. Sadly the hapless Master Gunner Ross severely injured one of his legs when the gun had recoiled.

It was late in the season, so they wasted no time in resuming their journey to Ireland.

By the time John and his party reached Mew Island the weather had already started to deteriorate. Nevertheless, they managed to make a few exploratory dives in dangerously rough conditions close in to shore where the waves were crashing over the jagged granite rocks. The lateness in the season did however bring one advantage. The seaweed that normally obscured the bottom throughout the summer had died away, revealing the rocky gullies that hid the treasure. The water was wonderfully clear and shafts of sunlight played about on the sand and rocks all around him. It reminded John of his childhood when he had played in rock-pools at the seaside, utterly fascinated with the variety of colourful and mysterious life-forms they harboured. There was also the occasional bonus when he came across a juicy lobster or edible crab crouched in a hole, waiting to be collected and cooked for dinner.

First they found some unrecognisable rusting iron debris jammed into the rocky crevices, but then, by pushing their hands down into the sand they even found some loose silver dollars to whet their appetite. No sooner had they discovered the site of the wreck than the weather closed in and they were forced to abandon their diving and take shelter in nearby Donaghadee harbour. It was not practical to wait for any short spells of good weather that might occur over the winter so they reluctantly turned their backs on the treasure and set sail for home. It was a tough voyage in hazardous conditions but they just about managed to get back in one piece.

Over the winter months, there was only one thing on their minds, the *Enterprise*. The silver dollars were sitting there, just waiting to be picked up. Or perhaps they had inadvertently revealed the existence of the secret hoard of treasure to the local community during their brief visit. Would the treasure still be there for them when they returned? The suspense was tantalising for John. With many unanswered questions reeling around in his head, John single-mindedly ensured that he had everything in place ready for a major treasure expedition as soon as the good weather returned.

At the first sign of spring the *Enterprise* expedition set sail again from Whitstable harbour. There were now three diving boats in the treasure hunting flotilla. The extra divers included two brothers, John and Thomas Gann of Whitstable, and William Wood of Herne Bay. John still felt duty-bound to include Charles and so invited him along as well.

They sailed straight past the Scilly Isles without stopping and turned north up St George's Channel towards the Irish Sea. They only interrupted the voyage briefly when necessary to restock with essential supplies of food and water before continuing on their journey. There was no time to lose. On arrival at Mew Island they went straight to work, hoping and praying that the locals had not already cleaned up.

Their luck had held out and it was not long before the silver coins started to arrive on the surface. Over the first series of dives they mapped out the fairly wide distribution of the treasure and then concentrated on collecting from the centre outwards. The silver landed in the boats in ever increasing quantities. John was well aware he would need to clean up the treasure as quickly as possible because once the word got out in the local community that such riches were being harvested, they would probably need to leave in a hurry. So he sent for reinforcements from Whitstable. No sooner had the invitations been received than two more boats hastily set off to assist in the scramble for the silver dollars.

As the story of the fabulous hoard of treasure was whispered amongst the boatmen in Whitstable, some became envious and even hostile at having not been invited to join in the feast. Amongst these was a sneaky, spying Mr Harris who was clearly jealous of not having received an invitation to the party. There was a good reason he hadn't been invited. He simply couldn't be trusted. He had a reputation for dishonesty and he was the sort who would tip off the Preventive Service if he heard of any smuggled brandy coming ashore. Harris secretly drew up a list of the boats and the names of the crews that had gone off to Ireland and sent them to the Admiralty in London. At the same time he volunteered his services to maintain a close watch on those involved after their return. He was hoping that the divers would lose their claim to the treasure, perhaps they may even be arrested and clapped in irons. That would teach them not to leave him behind the next time.

It came as a shock to Harris when the Admiralty politely informed him that they had no interest in the matter whatsoever. The wreck was not that of a Royal Navy ship so the Admiralty had no jurisdiction. Then to his even greater dismay, Harris discovered that neither the ship nor its contents had been insured, so Lloyds were not interested either. It got worse. The silver had been privately owned. The owners of the slave trading ship were no longer in business and dealing in slaves had been outlawed in the British Empire since 1807. So there were no other claimants to the treasure.

It was finders keepers! Harris's devious plot had failed and he skulked away, disappearing back into the dark alleyways of Whitstable.

John's treasure hunting fleet in Ireland was operating out of the small harbour town of Donaghadee though they kept their presence there to a minimum. Maintaining the secrecy about the haul of treasure was paramount, but it was impossible to keep the raising of a vast hoard of silver a secret in such a small fishing community. It was inevitable that the locals would eventually catch on to what they were up to.

When this ultimately happened, as expected, it was not a good thing. After all, the treasure belonged to the locals. It was on *their* patch. So it just was not right that these strangers appeared out of nowhere and helped themselves to *their* silver. Predictably the matter escalated and soon got out of hand. Local boatmen sailed out to Mew Island in force and started interfering with the salvage work. They attacked the Whitstable boats, throwing rocks and anything else they could lay their hands on. Initially the Whitstablers tolerated the aggression but the attacks steadily grew in ferocity until they were forced to leave to avoid serious injuries.

Fortunately, a large quantity of silver had by then been recovered. John and Charles gathered it all together into one boat and they made their escape eastwards across the Irish Sea to Portpatrick on the west coast of Scotland, only a day's sailing away.

Once on the other side, they offloaded their cargo and William Edwards set sail once more for Whitstable leaving John and Charles to accompany the treasure hoard to London. John hastily hired a stagecoach to take them and their heavy booty to London, hoping that the unusually heavy baggage didn't attract too much attention. There was £24,000's worth of silver loaded onto the coach (about £1.7m in today's money!). The coach journey took four long days of tough riding, sat on hard seats in a bucking stagecoach. Fortunately the guard never needed to fire his blunderbuss to discourage any highwaymen during the journey. The age of the highwayman had fortunately drawn to a close. The last recorded case of highway robbery in Britain had been two years previously.

They were relieved, sore and exhausted by the time they arrived at the bank in London and offloaded their hoard of silver. They had slept very little over the past four days.

The Deane brothers and the crews of the diving boats had struck it rich though as it had turned out, it had not been without great risk. The attacks of the Donaghadee fishermen on the diving boats had been so vicious that John had on occasions feared for his life. So when he returned to Ramsgate he immediately obtained a licence from the customs authority to carry guns to protect himself in any future treasure hunting expedition.

When the divers who had attended the *Enterprise* expedition eventually turned their share of the treasure into cash, they invested it in a variety of ways. John Gann built a row of houses along the beach, which he named Copeland Cottages though it was later changed to Dollar Row. His brother Thomas Gann built a large house at the end of the row, which he called Copeland House. When John Gann finally retired from diving he knocked two of the end houses of Dollar Row into one and opened it as the King's Head beer house. It immediately became established as the "house of call" for the local divers. William Wood invested his money on retirement in a public house in Herne Bay, which he called the Diver's Arms. Surprisingly all these properties survive to this day though only the Diver's Arms is still selling beer.

Copeland House is one of those more interesting properties along the shore that has a secret cellar. By some strange coincidence, the joists either side of the concealed hatch have been cut in such a way that a brandy barrel just manages to slip through. Another carefully guarded secret is that the beer cellar under the Diver's Arms had a hidden tunnel below ground level which opened into an adjacent water culvert. So if a smuggler hypothetically climbed into the culvert opening on the beach, any Preventive Service officers waiting to catch him coming out the other end would be disappointed, as he could slip sideways into the Diver's Arms cellar whilst out of sight. He would have mysteriously disappeared. Unfortunately the local magistrate got to hear of it and William Wood was ordered to brick it up again.

John Deane bought himself a magnificent sailing sloop, the *Mary*. He was wisely re-investing his share of the proceeds in his prospering diving business. Charles moved house from a rather humble residence off the Old Kent Road to a somewhat grander house in St Mary Newington, closer again into London, but further from the sea.

The Deane brothers had, at last, shown what riches there were to be won through the application of their diving helmet. Needless to say, this was nowhere more appreciated than amongst the privileged Whitstable boatmen who had attended the treasure hunt in Ireland. They were now chomping at the bit to get their hands on their own diving helmets having tasted the fruits of sunken treasure. They quite naturally wanted to seek their own fortunes rather than settle for just a percentage whilst on John's team.

George Bell, Thomas Gann and their legal representative, John Bethell, were the first to come knocking on Augustus Siebe's door in Denmark Street, Soho, to buy a set of diving equipment. Bethell was a top-flight lawyer who had been employed by the oyster dredgers in Whitstable in the past to resolve disputes over oyster grounds. So he was the obvious choice when a legal representative was needed. They had taken the wise precaution of first obtaining the permission of Edward Barnard to purchase the equipment to ensure there would be no complications with Charles's continued claims of patent protection. Siebe was delighted to oblige and manufactured the first set of helmet diving equipment that had not been specifically produced for the Deane brothers.

The global population of helmet divers had now reached about a dozen. They were into double figures.

Siebe was quick to recognise he had an important new product to add to his already successful product range. But he perhaps did not notice the unusually close attention John Bethell was paying to his manufacturing techniques. He was strolling quietly around the crowded workshop, peering inquisitively over the shoulders of the craftsmen as they worked at their lathes and benches. He was extra careful not to touch anything or any of the workers in case his immaculate clothes were soiled in any way. He had an expensive taste in clothes and the way he dressed reflected his vanity. He found the strong smell of the lubricating oil used on the lathes to be particularly obnoxious so he tried to protect himself by holding a large silk handkerchief to his nose. His inspection however, was suspiciously detailed for someone from the legal profession. Bethell was a cunning, ambitious and dangerous man. He was all the more dangerous because he was wealthy and highly influential. His older brother was Richard Bethell, Lord Westbury, who was later to become Lord Chancellor, in charge of the country's finances.

Following the visit to Denmark Street, Bethell concluded his legal services for Bell and Gann as expected, ensuring that the purchase of the diving equipment went through smoothly. But he didn't stop there. He had secretly become interested in the tales of sunken treasure and decided he should have a share of it. Not having much time for scruples, as soon as he got back to his office at 14 Lincolns Inn Fields he plotted to get in on the act and to go into competition with his clients.

Lincolns Inn Fields is the legal centre of London, dating back to Roman times. It is London's largest residential square with a beautiful garden surrounded by prestigious buildings including that of the Royal College of Surgeons. The lawyers who had offices there, were (and still are) amongst the most accomplished and, of course, expensive in the country. Sir John Soane the architect who built the Bank of England had lived next door to Bethell at number 13 and today is a museum dedicated to his memory. The gardens themselves hold many historical tales. In 1683 Lord Russell was executed there for his alleged involvement in a Popish plot to assassinate King Charles II. He was beheaded before a huge crowd. As tradition had it, as he stood before the gathered crowd, he gave the executioner ten guineas to encourage him to make a clean and swift job of it. Unfortunately it didn't work out that way and he needed four strokes of the axe to complete the decapitation. When asked why four strokes had been necessary, the executioner excused himself by saying "His Lordship moved". His Lordship had presumably stopped moving by the fourth stroke. A hundred years previously, fourteen men who had been convicted of plotting against Elizabeth I were executed in the square by hanging, drawing and quartering, hopefully in that order.

Being a patent agent as well as a lawyer, Bethell was well aware of the potential objection to his making a copy of the Deane dress. Though he was confident he could quash any such objection, the delay caused by the litigation process, which could take several years, would be inconvenient to him. So the simplest way for him to join in the treasure diving business was to produce a diving helmet of a slightly different design.

The following year, 1835, he handed in the specification for his diving dress design at the Patent Office. He had just joined the sunken treasure hunting club.

With that done, he went on to fund several ambitious treasure hunting expeditions. The first was along the well-worn path to the *Lutine* off Holland and the second was to a one-hundred-year-old wreck in Cornwall. Both ventures were disastrous failures. His money was entirely wasted. But by now he had succumbed to 'gold fever' (as well as the very similar condition 'silver fever') and all caution went out of the window.

So he next set his sights on the wreck of HMS *Athenien*, a 3rd-rate frigate sunk on the infamous Esquerques Rocks in the Mediterranean. These notorious rocks come up from nowhere and stop just beneath the surface in the middle of the sea, out of sight of land, half way between Sicily and the North African coast. Many ships have sailed unsuspectingly into them and promptly disappeared. Their very existence was even disputed because few of the people who had come across them had survived. Shortly before the *Athenien* struck, the Captain and First Mate were having an argument about their existence. The Captain argued they did not exist, to which the mate replied that if they did exist, this is where they would be. It was not a long while later that the Captain was bobbing around in the ship's long-boat in the open sea, where he had to concede to the First Mate he had been right all along.

The *Athenien* had gone down with a cargo of silver allegedly worth $3,500,000. But Bethell soon lost interest in that one when he found that she had drifted off the reef and sunk in over 1,000 feet of water.

Bethell did however enjoy a brief period of success, supplying eight sets of his diving equipment to the Admiralty and a few to private individuals. But his equipment lacked the professional touch. Its design and construction failed because of his lack of familiarity with nautical matters or feedback from its users. In short, it was amateurish. It could not withstand the rigours of heavy usage in an aggressive environment and it was not 'sailor proof'. After a few short years, the market for his equipment dried up. Unfortunately, the failure of Bethell's diving equipment did not help the credibility of the new art in the eyes of the Admiralty and even reinforced their scepticism.

Both John and Charles were by now feeling much more confident about their own diving capabilities. John in particular was building on his earlier successes. He was effectively independent of others and he was now ready to take on any salvage venture. Despite his growing independence, John tried to maintain a working relationship with Charles. Charles himself was heavily dependent on John's support though he hid that as best he could. Indeed, he played on John's loyalty, constantly reminding him how much John owed to his smoke dress idea.

They decided that their next collaborative project should be closer to home and since the *Boyne* was now out of bounds, they should make a more serious attempt to recover the valuable cannons remaining on the *Royal George*, off Portsmouth. Their previous expedition to the *Royal George* four years earlier, though partially successful, had identified a weakness in the air pump design. They had had difficulty achieving an adequate pressure to deliver air to the greater depth. But now they had an improved air pump produced by Augustus Siebe and the *Royal George* was within range.

Charles still had the Admiralty's permission to work on the wreck. So he came to a commercial arrangement with John, who had established a firm business partnership with William Edwards of Whitstable. They would use John's boat, the *Mary* to return to the *Royal George*.

The relationship between Charles and John was holding together, just.

10
HMS Royal George revisited

The brothers were on board John's new sloop, the *Mary*, berthed in Whitstable harbour in October 1834. They were hastily preparing to sail to Portsmouth to recommence their operations on the *Royal George* and catch the last few days of the summer. Charles had come from London to help with the preparations.

The *Mary* was dwarfed in amongst the lofty two-masted brigs and brigantines that were crowding the tiny harbour. The coal trade was expanding rapidly and with so many ships now trading through Whitstable it was getting difficult to get a space at the harbour wall. Several brigantines were riding at anchor offshore and their masters were clamouring to enter harbour. The *Mary* was holding up the unloading of the larger ships and heated exchanges were taking place with the Harbourmaster.

One of the problems with the harbour was that the movements of the larger ships could only take place around high water because when the tide dropped it was too shallow for them to move. They simply had to sit there on the mud and wait. This meant another twelve-hour delay if they missed a high water opportunity.

It was also a dirty job working around the harbour. The daily unloading of hundreds of tons of coal by hand, generated clouds of coal dust that settled everywhere. Nothing escaped the fine black powder. The seamen looked as though they had been working down a coalmine by the time they were finished for the day. The longer John spent hanging around in the harbour, the filthier he, his boat and equipment became, so he was as anxious as anyone to get out.

The *Royal George* was such an attractive proposition to anyone who had the ability to work on the wreck, that the Admiralty received a continuous flow of applications requesting their permission to carry out salvage work on it. Over many years, they routinely turned down all the offers because nobody was able to convince them that they could do the job. It is no surprise that nothing had been done to clear the wreck for fifty years. The vast majority of the offers varied from the impractical to the bizarre. Add to that a highly sceptical and bureaucratic Admiralty and you have the perfect recipe for procrastination.

The main problem had always been the great depth, some ninety feet of water, in which the ship lay. Charles had been very privileged to have been given the opportunity to work on her two years previously and that was only because he had actually demonstrated a credible diving capability.

However, Charles had been absent from the wreck for two years and the Admiralty were now receiving offers from people who claimed to have the same capability as John and Charles. Not being aware of Charles's plans, the Admiralty sent him a letter asking him if he intended to continue to work on the wreck. The letter eventually caught up with Charles onboard the *Mary* at Whitstable, from where he sent an urgent reply.

He explained that he had been away in Scotland. He added that he had previously not had the funds to continue his work on the wreck but now he was about to set sail for Portsmouth to recommence his diving operation. As ever, he made no mention of John's involvement.

To everyone's relief, the *Mary* eventually cast off and sailed out of the harbour. They had over two hard days of sailing and finally arrived in Portsmouth on 29th October with John, Charles, William Edwards and two other Whitstablers, Stephen and Thomas Richards aboard. It was late in the season so John wasted no time in getting in the water.

Their success was instant. Literally the following day, Charles wrote to the Admiralty saying *he* had just recovered two bronze 24-pounders, each weighing over two and half tons and over ten and a half feet long. In actual fact John had raised one and Charles the other. The value they eventually expected to achieve when they handed the two guns over to the Admiralty was upwards of £400 (£28,000 by today's standards). This was based on the value that John had previously achieved for the guns from the Ordnance Transport Vessel *Guernsey Lily* off Great Yarmouth. By the end of November, John had landed three more *Royal George* cannons at the Gunwharf in Portsmouth Dockyard. The expected total value had risen to £1,000 (£70,000 today).

Charles was becoming more disturbed with each successive dive. The gloom and darkness that permanently shrouded the wreck was becoming overwhelmingly oppressive to him. He started making all sorts of excuses for not getting back in the water, leaving John to all the diving work. He finally returned home to London on the pretext that he needed to be back with his family. John and William Edwards were lucky with the weather and they continued their diving operations until the end of December, during which time a sixth 24-pounder was recovered.

When the cannons first arrived on the surface they looked hardly recognisable, with a thin covering of brown algae and mud. They didn't smell too healthy either. A connoisseur might have described it as having the rich aroma of the sea with subtle overtones of something dead and rotting. But with hard scrubbing and a plentiful supply of seawater, the smooth bronze surface eventually shone through. The bronze guns were in perfect condition despite their immersion of over fifty years and by the time they had finished scrubbing, they looked like new once more.

Curious officers from Nelson's flagship HMS *Victory,* which was moored in Portsmouth harbour, visited John's sloop to inspect the guns. They were so impressed with their good condition that they actually fired one to prove it.

John was now working full time on the *Royal George* and he was missing his family who were a long way away in Ramsgate. He eventually resolved that the Portsmouth area was a better location at which to base his future operations so he moved his family down. The most convenient location was the ancient fortified town of Gosport, on the western side of Portsmouth harbour where he could also find a sheltered mooring for his boat. There he was in the heart of the local fishing community where he could always find any additional crew he might need and all the skills required to maintain his boat. He looked around for a suitable property and settled on a terraced house at 72 North Street in Gosport, just a two-minute walk from the shore. From there he could give the *Royal George* his undivided attention.

The Deanes were expecting a handsome and badly needed payment for the salvaged guns from the Admiralty. They had been working on the *Royal George* for two whole months and had not yet received a penny for their efforts. But then there was a hiccup

When they pressed the Admiralty for their payment they discovered that the Admiralty didn't own the guns. They were actually the property of the Board of Ordnance with whom Charles had no financial agreement. For a moment, it looked as though the two months of operations on the *Royal George* had been for nothing. Fortunately, the Ordnance turned out to be not only quite reasonable, but briefly showed great generosity. They said that if the Deanes dropped off the sixth gun they had recovered at the Tower of London they would allow them to keep the other five.

John dutifully delivered the gun to the Tower and the deal was done. It was an excellent arrangement. The Deanes could now sell the guns for much more than their mere scrap metal value as they had immense historic value.

There were serious collectors around who were desperate to own an example or two of these magnificent weapons. At the top of this list was the eccentric, but extremely wealthy, John Powell of Quex Park in Kent. He had already bought several cannons from John, which he had raised from the *Guernsey Lily*. Powell had an insatiable appetite for cannons. He collected them the same way some people collected paintings. John whetted Powell's appetite with a free gift of a 24-pound shot together with its wad and tampion, extracted from one of the guns. The marketing ploy worked a treat. Powell was hooked and soon became the proud owner of two beautiful 24-pounder bronze cannons from the *Royal George*. They can still be seen today at Quex Park museum, amongst the many other cannons which Powell accumulated.

Charles also exploited the *Royal George* guns to advantage, though his agenda was slightly different from John's. Charles saw in the *Royal George* an opportunity to promote his name and reputation in London. For him, the *Royal George* was his long-awaited path to fame. The *Royal George* was going to be his launch pad to stardom.

In 1835, at enormous and foolhardy personal expense, he opened a prestigious submarine exhibition in the Cosmorama in fashionable Regent Street. The Cosmorama was a special type of exhibition showing popular scenes and landscapes from different parts of the world using clever optical and lighting effects. Charles chose the premises specially to display his exhibits because of its popularity with visiting high society. He had lavishly commissioned twenty oil paintings by a prominent marine painter named Meadows, covering nearly 1,400 square feet of canvass. They illustrated a variety of his diving operations, including diving on HMS *Boyne* and HMS *Royal George*. Money was no object. He even published a book entitled *Submarine Researches* illustrating his diving on the *Royal George* in "his improved diving apparatus" as well as many of his other diving projects, and still there was not one mention of his brother John.

The main exhibit was one of the magnificent bronze 24-pounder guns from the *Royal George*. A variety of smaller artefacts from the wreck were also on display, including a large iron cooking cauldron still containing the petrified remains of beef bones stuck to the bottom which were being stewed at the moment the ship went down. There were pewter plates, cannon shot, bottles, shoes, ropes, chains and iron bolts. And of course, there was a complete set of diving equipment on view.

His Majesty King William IV honoured Charles's exhibition with a visit. The King and his entourage filled the exhibition. His Majesty became so fascinated that he gave directions that if a sufficient number of the bronze guns could be recovered, he wanted a battery formed of them at Windsor Castle. Charles proudly described the many exhibits. This was the ultimate accolade for Charles's exhibition and he quickly renamed it The *Royal* Submarine Exhibition. Charles's dream was coming true. The *Royal George* was proving to be his most prized possession.

Nick-named the Sailor King because of his earlier naval career, King William IV reigned for only seven years having come to the throne at the late age of 64 years. But he did manage to see in the abolition of slavery in the British Empire and to father ten illegitimate children with an actress named Dorothea Blaire. He had no legitimate children of his own when he died in 1837 so his young niece Princess Victoria assumed the throne and suddenly change was in the air.

Distinguished visits to Charles's *Royal* exhibition were also made by several Lords of the Admiralty as well as Admiral Sir Philip Henderson Durham GCB, Commander-in-Chief at Portsmouth. He had a special interest in the exhibition. He had fought alongside Nelson at Trafalgar and in his younger days, as an up-and-coming acting-Lieutenant, he had actually been on board the *Royal George* when she sank in 1782. He was Officer of the Watch at the time and therefore lucky enough to have been on deck. He was one of only two of the ship's officers to survive and had been rescued from the water, half-drowned, by a boat sent over from HMS *Victory,* which was anchored nearby.

On the wreck itself, as the more accessible guns were raised, John was finding it more and more difficult to maintain the flow. By 1836 his exertions to recover cannons were proving markedly less fruitful. There were plenty more guns to be recovered, but they were imbedded too far inside the wreck.

In total he had raised twenty bronze and eight iron guns from the wreck over the preceding three years. The Ordnance were now taking all the cannons from him as they were landed at the Gunwharf, but paying him only half their value. This was a serious blow to the Deanes because they had been originally assured by the Admiralty that they would receive the full value of the guns.

It was looking as though the *Royal George* operation was coming to an end.

John was acutely aware that he needed to maintain his income, and with the *Royal George* operation no longer being cost-effective, he had to find another project. So he turned his attention once more to marketing his diving equipment. Perhaps if he could sell enough diving sets, that would keep him going between diving projects. With the appearance of competitive designs, especially Bethell's, coming on the market, it was becoming increasingly important to hold the high ground and remain the principal supplier.

John introduced an important accessory to accompany his equipment, which gave him a significant marketing advantage. He had realised that anyone buying a new set of his equipment and wanting to start diving would need some form of instruction. So in 1836 he settled down at his home in Gosport to write the first ever diving manual. He subsequently provided a free copy with every new set of equipment he sold. Its title was the "Method of using Deane's Patent Diving Apparatus". In the introduction he wrote:

"Messrs. C. A. and J. Deane beg to caution the public against spurious copies of their invention, the Diving Apparatus; such copies being very bad imitations of the same, have, in almost every instance, failed of being either safe or effective. Messrs. C. A. and J. Deane, therefore, beg to say, that none are genuine but those constructed under their own immediate inspection, which are approved and warranted, with instructions supplied for their use."

John's manual described the equipment in detail, how the diver should dress into it, how it should be cared for and maintained and also provided details of a set of rope signals that the diver could use to communicate with his attendant on the surface. He explained how the equipment:

"will be found to be very valuable in discovering sunken property, surveying wrecks, or sunken ships and vessels - as also the Foundations of Harbours, Piers, Docks, Bridges, etc., etc., etc."

The supply of diving equipment provided a useful background income but it didn't make enough to maintain his family and boat.

He urgently needed another profitable wreck.

11
The Mary Rose mystery

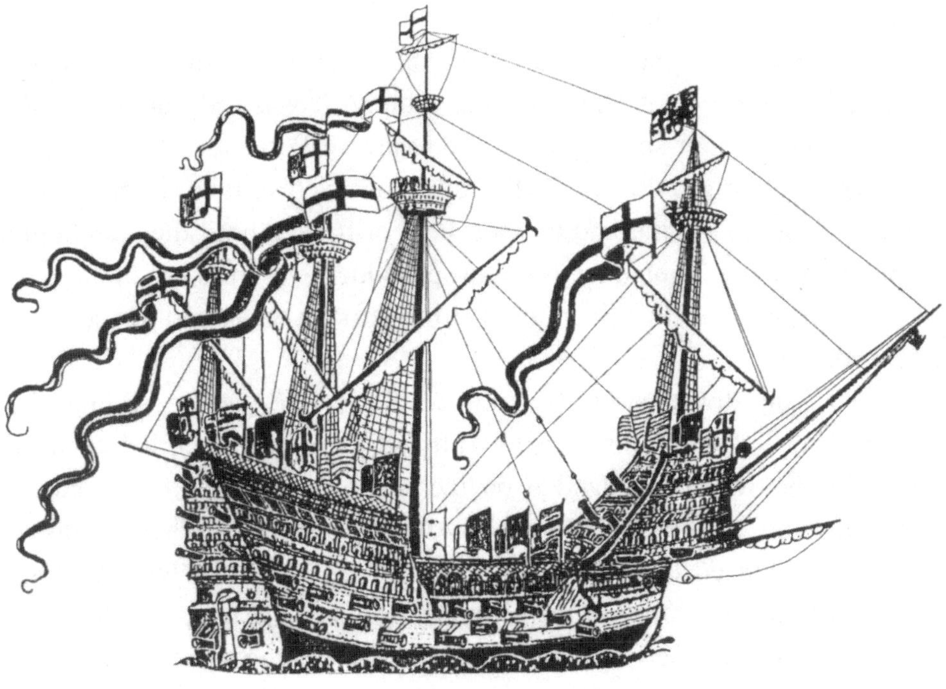

Local fishermen from Gosport had known for some time about a particular obstacle on the seabed in a relatively shallow part of the Solent known as Spitsand. It was a popular fishing ground and nets had periodically been fouled on the obstacle. But when they swept in an attempt to lift it, they were never successful. Whatever it was, it was big and sunk deep into the seabed.

It had been a bit of a mystery for as long as anyone could remember.

The fishermen knew Henry Abbinett quite well and when a small group of them learnt that he had acquired a diving helmet and was able to investigate obstacles on the seabed, they thought they might be able to solve the mystery and perhaps even earn some money. If the object turned out to have some value, then they could all have a share of it.

Abbinett was willing to give it a go and he and his diver sailed out to investigate. The water depth was about fifty feet but the underwater visibility was not good, only two to three feet. The seabed was soft mud, covered in shells and weed.

The fishermen had marked the position of the obstacle by snagging a rope on it and attaching a buoy. It was only about a mile outside the harbour so they had a good view of Portsea to the north and the Isle of Wight to the south. The tide was slack so they dropped their anchor a little up-wind and let their boat drift back until they could get hold of the buoy. Then they threw a rope ladder over the stern of the boat next to the buoy so the diver could climb into the water and down to the seabed.

The diver carefully climbed down the ladder sliding the buoyed rope through his arm, as Abbinett paid out the coiled air hose and lifeline. The diver landed on the seabed and instantly stirred up the soft mud, so the limited visibility he had enjoyed on the way down was now reduced to nothing. He was in total darkness. Nevertheless, he began to grope around the obstacle which as far as he could make out was a large piece of old timber. It was sticking a few feet out of the seabed and it was covered in weed, barnacles and something very slimy. He couldn't identify any particular shape to it and decided it was worthless. He thought it was probably the remains of an old hulk, so he gave it up as a bad job and climbed back up the ladder to the surface. He ponderously climbed back into the boat and sat down, breathless from his exertions. Abbinett helped to remove his helmet and when the diver had got his breath back he described what he had found. Everyone was understandably quite disappointed. They recovered their buoy-line and headed back in to Portsmouth harbour, dismayed that they had wasted half a day on a wild goose chase.

In the small town of Gosport it was not long before the story of the old wooden foul circulated amongst the fishermen and eventually reached John Deane. At the time, John was becoming frustrated with the diminishing productivity of his labours on the *Royal George*, so it did not take much to persuade himself to investigate the mystery obstacle himself. He contacted the fishermen and arranged for them to lead him back to the obstruction so he could dive on it. They struck a deal whereby they would share the value of anything he brought up equally between the two parties.

John dived on the mystery object and quickly confirmed that it really was a piece of old timber stuck in the seabed. He pondered that since it was such a large piece, it must have belonged to a large ship. It could even be the stump of a ship's mast. If there was a large ship sunk in the mud beneath him, there should be more of it sticking up clear of the mud somewhere around him. So he decided to investigate further. He took his distance line that was tied to the bottom of the rope ladder and waded off over the muddy seabed to search for any other artefacts. Clouds of black mud billowed from beneath his boots as he slowly trudged over the bottom. He had walked about fifty feet when he saw a dark shadow loom up in front of him. He stopped to see if it moved, but thankfully it didn't, so he approached it slowly. As he got within a few feet of it he was able to make out the muzzle of a cannon sticking upright, four feet out of the seabed. He took out his knife, cut away the weed that was attached around the muzzle and scraped the metal surface. He immediately recognised the yellowish glint of bronze.

He could hardly believe his eyes.

John tied off his distance line on the cannon and followed it back to the ladder. He climbed up and got back into his boat. Everybody on board was delighted with the news and they quickly made preparations for lifting the cannon. John dived again and secured a strong lifting rope to the gun, and the heaving began.

The seabed was initially reluctant to give up the gun but with some gentle persuasion, using the boat to haul in different directions, its stubborn grip was broken. When the cannon eventually reached the surface, they were no longer surprised at tightness of the grip with which the seabed had held on to it. Another eight feet of the cannon had been buried in the mud. The bronze gun was a total of twelve feet in length and weighed three tons.

John was mightily pleased with the potential scrap value of three tons of bronze, but there was an even bigger shock in store for him. He landed the cannon at the Gunwharf, Portsmouth harbour, on 16th June 1836.

A dockside crane lifted the gun out of the boat and landed it ashore. Immediately a small crowd gathered around as he set about cleaning off the sticky mud and barnacles to expose the clean smooth bronze surface. He scraped and scrubbed and as the smelly coating washed away he could see the cannon was in remarkably good condition and spectacularly ornate. The lugs or dolphins, which are two lifting handles on either side of the barrel, would normally have been shaped like dolphins. But these were unusually shaped as lions' heads. There was an armorial badge cast on the barrel and it consisted of a rose encircled by a garter, with a thistle at the top. It had a Latin inscription which began "HENRICVS. VIII ...". Translated, the full inscription read "Henry VIII, King of England, France and Ireland, Invincible Defender of the Faith".

Instantly he realised there was something more than just scrap value here.

Representatives of the Civil Offices at Portsmouth soon appeared out of nowhere and barged their way officiously through the crowd to examine the gun closely. They also recognised the significance of John's trophy immediately and pounced on the gun. Nobody was allowed to go near it, touch it of move it without their permission. They hurriedly marched back to their offices and promptly wrote to the Board of Ordnance, carefully quoting the gun's unique inscription.

It seemed incredible, but it soon had to be admitted that John Deane had discovered the wreck of the long lost *Mary Rose*, Henry VIII's own flagship sunk in 1545, nearly 300 years previously. On the day she had gone down she had been leading a British fleet out of Portsmouth harbour to engage a massive French invasion fleet coming round the eastern side of the Isle of Wight. The two fleets had faced up to each other and then joined in battle. The French made the first move, firing their huge long range guns from their rowed galleys. The *Mary Rose* moved in closer to the French ships and unleashed her broadside from her port guns. Then she turned about to fire a second broadside from her starboard guns but before that happened, she suddenly filled with water and sank in front of thousands of disbelieving British and French soldiers and sailors, not to mention King Henry himself.

The argument has raged for 500 years to this day as to whether she sank as a result of having been hit by French shot or because her recently fitted lower gun ports were still open when she tacked and had gone below the surface of the water. Naturally, the French version is that they sank her. Whatever the cause, the ship had gone down with nearly all hands and the French claimed it as a victory. After a few more exchanges of shot the French changed their minds, turned around and went home, blaming the weather as unsuitable for an invasion.

The knowledge of the existence of the *Mary Rose* disappeared into the sands of time and the mud of the Solent over the ensuing 300 years. That is, until John Deane landed Henry VIII's bronze cannon at the Gunwharf.

Now John Deane had a King's ship to explore!

There was just one problem. Whatever remained of the priceless ship was completely buried in the seabed. Nevertheless, a furore ensued. Letters flew backwards and forwards between Royalty, the Admiralty and the Board of Ordnance. The matter had to be dealt with very carefully and of course with due protocol.

Meanwhile, John was intensifying his investigations on the wreck site. He scoured the seabed for more clues and relics. He marched up and down, prodding a steel spike, six feet long, deep into the mud to trace out the extent of the wreck and to try to find more artefacts. He was rewarded with finding two more bronze guns and two iron guns which were of a peculiar design. The fishermen assisted with the recovery of one of each of these. All four guns were landed at the Gunwharf and dutifully handed over to the Ordnance authorities.

One evening, the five fishermen who had originally put John onto the wreck site and assisted in recovering some of the cannons knocked on his door and pressed him for their share of the value of the guns. John explained he had not yet been paid for the guns and he had no way of valuing them. He tried to explain that he was in the hands of the Ordnance when it came to valuations. In good faith he advanced twenty-five pounds to the fishermen, but surprisingly this did not satisfy them and the fishermen escalated their protest. They petitioned Sir Frederick Maitland, the Admiral Superintendent of Portsmouth Dockyard, pleading that they were not being fairly treated by John.

Sir Frederick who was of Scottish extraction, had an interesting track record in the field of arbitration. Twenty-one years previously, he had intercepted Napoleon at Rochefort in France as he was trying to escape to America after his defeat at Waterloo. He had then negotiated Napoleon's surrender and personally transported him back to England in his ship HMS *Bellerophon*.

John counter-claimed against the fishermen's petition to Sir Frederick. He laid all the facts out in the fullest detail and proposed a reasonable arrangement. Sir Frederick's judgement was as fair as it could be. He suggested that John should pay the fishermen half the value of the guns, which they had assisted in recovering and one third the value of any guns they had not assisted with, the value being whatever the Government chose to award. Furthermore, the fishermen would have no claim on John for anything he recovered that was not claimed by the Government.

That at last satisfied the fishermen, but that was not the end of the matter.

John was then surprised to learn that his friend Henry Abbinett had added his name to the list of claimants to the *Mary Rose*. Abbinett had also requested the Admiralty that he should be allowed to work on the wreck. He claimed it was he himself who had first dived down to the *Mary Rose* under the direction of the Gosport fishermen. However, because the obstruction he found on the sea bed was covered in weed he had chosen to come back later, when the weed would have died off. And John Deane had unfortunately intervened whilst he was away.

John's response was that, amongst other things, Abbinett already had the rights to work on the wreck of HMS *Boyne*, his brother Charles had the rights to work on the wreck of HMS *Royal George*, but he didn't have any wreck of his own on which to work.

Sir Frederick proved himself to be a fair mediator once again. He awarded John the exclusive rights to work on the wreck of the *Mary Rose*. So now Abbinett, Charles and John each had a wreck of his own to work on. One of the immediate consequences was that John's diving operations on the *Royal George* ceased having been working on that particular wreck only on behalf of Charles who had chosen to stop working on it himself.

John dived on the *Mary Rose* for the remainder of 1836 but he eventually ran out of relics to salvage. He knew there were more artefacts to be found buried deep in the mud. Unfortunately he had no way of excavating into the wreck so he had to give up the project, at least until he could find a way of digging deep into the mud.

The next big opportunity for John arose early in 1838 when he heard that a wreck obstructing the navigation of the river Thames near Gravesend needed to be got rid of. This was the brig *William,* which had sunk whilst carrying a full cargo of coal. Brigs were large, two-masted ships capable of carrying substantial cargoes, though the *William* was no ordinary brig. She was actually a retired brig of war, so not only was it a large obstruction, it was also a sturdily built one. It was not going to be an easy matter to break up her hull to clear her away.

At that time, the responsibility for maintaining the navigability of the river Thames rested with the Lord Mayor of London. He was the Head Conservator. The Mayor initially asked the Admiralty to remove the wreck but an embarrassed Admiralty had to concede that they lacked the capability. The Mayor next went to Colonel Charles William Pasley, Director of the Royal Engineers at Chatham, from whom he received a more positive response.

As it happened Pasley had been experimenting with laying explosive charges in shallow water for military applications for some time. He was actively investigating the subject, so he eagerly accepted the challenge. Pasley was a tenacious fighter of Scottish blood. He had a formidable list of technical achievements to his credit and a distinguished war record. One of his main weaknesses was his vanity, which grew in step with each promotion as he steadily climbed through the ranks.

During the height of the Napoleonic War he had been under the command of Lord Chatham when his forces were besieging the Dutch town of Flushing, which was occupied by the French. In the middle of the night of 14th August 1809, Pasley led a storming party against a French battery. During the surprise attack his men successfully spiked the French guns and captured fifty prisoners, but Pasley paid a high price. He was bayoneted in the thigh and then took a shot in the back.

Pasley's soldiers assumed he must have been killed and carried his blood-soaked body back to their lines. Against all the odds, Pasley survived the horrific wounds despite having a bullet lodged against his spine. After a whole year of convalescing an irrepressible Pasley was back in the saddle.

So when he was challenged to detonate explosives in water deeper than anyone had ever done before, Pasley was up for it. He researched the available resources and concluded that he needed to use a diving bell and, perhaps, even a diving helmet. Things should have developed swimmingly when he received a letter from John Deane offering his services. Pasley considered the offer carefully and asked the advice of a seafaring captain named William Kemp who had been involved in salvage operations in the Thames.

That proved to be a disastrous move. There were to be regrettable and even tragic consequences resulting from his poor choice of adviser.

Unfortunately, William Kemp bore a serious grudge against John because he had previously fallen out with him when John had turned down his request to assist in a salvage project. Kemp seized the opportunity to poison Pasley's opinion of John. Kemp cleverly gained Pasley's confidence by feeding his vanity and playing on his innate distrust of civilians and deep-rooted frugal nature. He managed to persuade Pasley that John would cheat him out of his money. As a result, Pasley unwisely turned down John's perfectly reasonable offer.

John was extremely disappointed because this was such an important opportunity to introduce his diving helmet to the military. So he then offered to carry out the work for no charge at all, and to just recover his expenses. What better deal could Pasley expect to get? But Kemp had done his malicious work so well that a distrusting Pasley even turned down John's offer of free diving services. As far as the paranoid Pasley was concerned, there had to be catch in there somewhere.

Pasley continued to be advised by Kemp and eventually went ahead with the clearance of the brig *William*. He successfully developed a technique for the detonation of gunpowder in the deepest part of the river, and the whole operation was a brilliant success.

That is, apart from Pasley losing one of his best men, a Corporal Henry Mitchell, who died in Kemp's diving helmet. Kemp had naively advised Pasley that no special training or experience was needed to use his diving equipment. Consequently Mitchell had been sent down in a strong current and zero visibility and had become hopelessly entangled in the tangled rigging of the wreck. He sadly died slowly from hypothermia as they had to wait six hours for the next slack water before they could recover his body using their diving bell.

Despite the blatant incompetence shown by Kemp in the inadequacy of his advice, which cost the life of Corporal Mitchell, Pasley bizarrely favoured him over John Deane.

Pasley paid dearly for his poor choice of adviser. He had abandoned his plan to use his own men as divers and reluctantly hired experienced civilian divers from Whitstable and Herne Bay to finish the job off, but pointedly ignoring John Deane.

Despite the fatal diving accident and his reliance on civilian divers, Pasley had covered himself in glory with the clearance of the brig *William*. The river Thames was freely navigable once more. London was back in business.

The Lord Mayor of London was overjoyed. He showered Pasley with gifts including a gold box valued at fifty guineas and to cap it all, the great honour of the Freedom of the City of London. But as far as the civilian divers who had actually done the work were concerned, they deserved nothing. In fact as far as Pasley was concerned, they had been overpaid. Pasley actually wrote in his diary, "No Whitstable or Herne Bay diver will ever impose on me again".

Meanwhile, John Deane spent nearly the whole of 1838 crawling all over the wreck of the *Royal George*, picking up small artefacts here and there, but unfortunately no more cannons nor anything of significant value. Everything that was accessible from the outside of the wreck had been picked clean. To make the venture profitable once more, the wreck now had to be split open. It was time to open up Pandora's box.

In December 1838, John applied to the Ordnance for some obsolete thirteen-inch mortar shells and gunpowder, which he planned to detonate inside the *Royal George*. The following year was going to be a momentous year for both John and Charles. The entire three-decker, 108-gun warship was going to be opened up like an oyster and laid out on the seabed for John to help himself to the contents.

But by the end of 1838, Colonel Pasley and his Royal Engineers had joined the ranks of underwater operatives. Pasley had had a smell of underwater success and had just developed an effective method of blasting in deep water. He could visualise a whole new engineering skill to add to the already extensive repertoire of the Royal Engineers. What he needed next was a challenging project with which he could hone and perfect this new capability.

It just had to be the *Royal George*.

There was no better project. It offered everything he wanted. It was in deep water; its removal would re-open one of the Navy's prime anchorages which had been denied them for over fifty years; it would be a prestigious and even spectacular operation; he could use the project to train a large number of his men in the new skills; the value of the recovered material would offset much of the costs; civilians would not be helping themselves to the public purse and it would certainly do his own career no harm at all.

But first, there was one little problem to overcome. Charles Deane was standing in his way. Charles still had an exclusive agreement with the Admiralty to work on the *Royal George*.

Standing between Colonel Pasley and his prime objective was not a healthy place to be.

Pasley lost no time in pulling influential strings around the Admiralty. He wrote to Captain J W Deane Dundas in the Admiralty emphasising persuasively that his main concern was "for the benefit of the anchorage". He fired a second, killer broadside with a letter to Lieutenant General Sir Frederick William Mulcaster KCH, the Inspector General of Fortifications. Charles was caught in a pincer movement. Pasley was a master tactician in military politics.

Poor Charles didn't stand a chance.

By March 1839 Charles had been informed that he had lost the rights to the *Royal George* and that Pasley would be taking over. Charles pleaded in vain with the Admiralty. On 8th April the Admiralty pronounced once-and-for-all, "My Lords cannot allow him to proceed any further".

Charles was utterly devastated. John had been just about to open Pandora's box for him when Pasley had ruthlessly snatched it away. Pasley had single-handedly, with one cruel blow, destroyed Charles's dream. It was the last straw for Charles. His tormented brain couldn't handle the disappointment and he went out of his mind. He became suicidal. Men in white coats came and took him away to Peckham House Lunatic Asylum. In fact, this was the second time his distraught family had called on them to take him away. Charles's mental health was progressively deteriorating.

It could have been worse. At least Peckham House was a private lunatic asylum. It cost £1..13s..6d per week to keep him there. The facilities were as good as could have been expected. They included a billiards room and a sumptuous recreation and entertainment hall, all set in beautifully landscaped gardens.

Pasley had eliminated the only obstacle in his path and now he was ready, in his own words, "to attack against the *Royal George*".

12
The Royal Engineers attack HMS Royal George

Colonel Pasley did his homework before opening his attack on the *Royal George*, as you would expect of a true professional. He used the actual words "attack against the *Royal George*" in his diary. His approach to any problem was always along military lines. Every project he undertook was like a military operation. He classified everyone he met as either friend or foe. He ate, slept and breathed military. Perhaps that is why he had such a problem dealing with civilians. He couldn't pull rank on civilians.

He gathered as much intelligence on the *Royal George* as he could, including her condition, situation and location on the seabed, the tides and what might be expected to remain within her hull, cannons especially. He meticulously investigated his options and what forces he had at his command. He was still wary about the effectiveness of the diving helmet. In particular, having to pay civilians to conduct the diving work was repugnant to him. The very thought of it sent his blood pressure through the roof. Psychologists probably have a special name for the syndrome.

Finally, Pasley prepared a detailed Battle Plan. He divided his campaign into eight major sectors:

1 The present state of the Royal George

The survey information indicated that parts of the wreck stood 33 to 36 feet above the seabed.

2 The present state of the stores supposed to remain within the wreck

The inventory of cannons that remained included 21 iron 32-pounders, 10 iron 12-pounders, 16 brass 24-pounders and 16 brass 12-pounders.

3 The mode of blowing the wreck to pieces

A variety of explosive charges were proposed which included four large charges of 2,500 pounds of gunpowder. They were to be detonated using Professor Daniell's Constant Voltaic Battery.

4 The mode of weighing the fragments

Pasley was planning to use men operating from a diving bell to lift the fragments to the surface. In his own words, it would be unsuitable to use "a Helmet Diver, who goes down alone, and whose operations are not seen, and cannot be checked by any other person". His deep-seated distrust of civilian divers was still festering.

5 The persons necessary to be employed

Apart from his own contingent of Royal Engineers and Royal Sappers and Miners, Pasley planned on hiring several bell divers. He even took into account the hiring of two civilian helmet divers but strictly on a part-time basis only. He wrote that "these would form the most expensive class of men employed". He stated that the divers he used on the brig *William* cost five and a half guineas a day. That included a sailing boat, a crew of six men, a diver and his diving apparatus. John Deane and Henry Abbinett of Gosport charged five guineas a day for a similar service. This charge was "so very high, that it would amount to an absolute prohibition against any helmet divers at all". Pasley did however acknowledge that John had expressed his willingness to work on lower terms, but he never bothered to follow up on the offer. He never gave John a single chance to demonstrate his abilities. In John he had the most experienced and best-qualified diver in the world, at his doorstep, and he couldn't see it. He could not bring himself to believe that John was anything but a cheat and a swindler. In any case, Pasley had in mind a way of paying civilians divers less, by employing them without their diving equipment. He would scrape around and provide that himself.

6 The probable expense of the operation

Pasley estimated this would not exceed £2,500.

7 The authority and means required for carrying on the work

This required an arrangement with the Admiralty and the Board of Ordnance.

8 The probable time of completing the operation

Pasley estimated the anchorage would become available to the Navy in 1840, that is, in less than two years.

It certainly looked like an excellent plan, on the surface.

Pasley therefore chose a diving bell as his main weapon of choice, despite its cumbrous nature, sensitivity to weather and tide, heavy demand on manpower and large surface craft, not to mention expense. He was of course aware that the tidal stream over the *Royal George* site could be very strong. So by the application of some inventive nautical technology, he decided to modify a standard cubical cast iron diving bell by adding two boat ends to it. At least it was the Admiralty's money he was spending and those greedy civilians were not getting anything.

His idea was that the improved hydrodynamic shape would allow the bell to be operated in a strong tidal stream without its wallowing around and being dragged away. Pasley envisaged that his special bell could work for twelve hours a day with three shifts of men.

The theory was good, in parts.

Pasley commissioned the building of two wooden pointed boat ends by the shipwrights at Chatham Dockyard and had them attached to a cast iron bell. The resultant monster bell, over twelve feet long and weighing several tons, was taken out to HMS *Anson*, moored in the river Medway near Gillingham. Using a heavily built davit, a gang of forty-nine seamen hoisted the bell out over the water and lowered it into the gently flowing river.

Just as the theory had predicted, the bell remained more stable than a conventional bell in the current. But the large gang of men and substantial lifting gear that were required to handle the bell were entirely impractical. And the monster bell also made the handling vessel even more unstable during launch and recovery in any sort of sea condition. To cut a long story short, Pasley's revolutionary boat-ended bell experiment was a dismal failure and a total waste of time and the taxpayer's money. But at least it hadn't been wasted on civilians.

Pasley underestimated the cost of the *Royal George* project by 400%, and the time to completion would take five years, not two as he had planned. He also miscalculated the usefulness of the diving bell, which had to be dispensed with, and the usefulness of the diving helmet, on which he eventually became totally dependent.

When Pasley abandoned his diving bell he found he had painted himself into a corner. The only other option open to him was to employ civilian helmet divers and the only place to get them, other than John Deane and Henry Abbinett at Gosport, was Whitstable and Herne Bay. But he had vowed he would *never, ever* use them again. So he grudgingly did the only thing he could do. He swallowed his pride, which needed a very big gulp indeed. He went back to Whitstable and hired two civilian divers to help him clear the *Royal George*, carefully sidestepping John Deane.

The divers he chose at Whitstable were George Hall and Hiram London, both of the "Deane school". This time he chose well.

To save money Pasley hired the two divers without their equipment. He rummaged around, begged, borrowed and all but stole whatever diving equipment he could lay his hands on. He ended up borrowing a diving dress from John Bethell and a second one from the Board of Ordnance. The second one, an unofficial copy of the Deane equipment, had been manufactured by James Sadler of Tooley Street in London and it was not up to the same standard as the Deane equipment manufactured by Siebe.

The divers tried to use the Bethell diving dress but found that it leaked badly, so they cut the jacket in half and used it as an open helmet together with a new india-rubber dress ordered from Macintosh in London. The modified arrangement worked in the same manner as the Deane open diving helmet. That was fine since it was similar to the configuration they were used to. The divers also found that the Bethell hand pump didn't deliver enough air, so they ditched it in favour of the marginally better Sadler pump. A second pump supplied by Sadler did not improve matters much. The divers found that at the deeper depths they were still not getting enough air. This meant that they had to slow down their physical effort otherwise they could become unconscious and drown. But at least the equipment was cheap.

Pasley was really scraping the bottom of the barrel in equipping the civilian divers. If he was not careful, his false economy could seriously jeopardise the success of his operation.

As a base for the diving operations over the wreck of the *Royal George*, Pasley borrowed a hulk from Portsmouth Dockyard, which was the cut-down remains of the frigate HMS *Success*. This was moored near the wreck and provided him with his headquarters and accommodation for his officers. He also borrowed two smaller hulks or lighters from the Dockyard, which he moored directly over the wreck. They provided the accommodation for the divers and crews as well as the diving platforms and lifting facilities for raising pieces of wreckage. Each of the two lighters supported one diver at a time on the wreck.

In spite of the bodged and second-rate diving equipment collected by Pasley, the two civilian divers, Hall and London, did a first class job throughout 1839. Pasley even added a third diver named John Fullager of Chatham to the team towards the end of the season. On days when the civilian divers were not required, Pasley got two of his own men to try out the diving equipment, namely Corporal Harris and Private William Reid. These two intrepid men managed to achieve a depth of ninety feet, which to be fair, was a considerable accomplishment.

Pasley's first attempts at detonating the explosive charges in the deep water around the *Royal George* did not all go according to plan. Misfires were frequent. The gunpowder casks often leaked and the seawater ruined vast quantities of valuable gunpowder. But as the season progressed, the methods improved and successful detonations were more consistently achieved. In due course Pasley became so confident in the reliability of the explosions that he decided to hold a special demonstration of a massive explosion for the benefit of visiting royals and dignitaries.

The time and date for the spectacular explosion was set for 2 pm, on 16th August 1839.

The event attracted sixty sailing craft and about three hundred open boats. The *Messenger* steamer carried His Royal Highness the Duke of Cambridge. Dignitaries entertained on board HMS *Blenheim* included Sir Humphrey and Lady Stenhouse, the Bishop of London and his family, the Earl of Dundonald, the Honourable Mrs Fleming, Sir John Hippsley, Miss Bolton (niece to the late Lord Nelson), and "a party of Wiltshire ladies".

The Earl of Dundonald was the famous 'Fighting' Admiral Thomas Cochrane who had fought gallantly in the Napoleonic Wars. During a period as a Member of Parliament he had been imprisoned on a false charge of fraud for which he was expelled from the Navy and Parliament. When he was released he went abroad and commanded successively the Chilean, Peruvian, Brazilian and Greek navies with distinction. He was then reinstated in the Royal Navy and received a Royal pardon.

A huge bomb consisting of a cylindrical vessel seven feet long and three feet in diameter had been specially built for Pasley at Portsmouth Dockyard. It was filled with a massive 2,900 pounds of gunpowder. At 1.30 pm the tide slacked off on schedule and the bomb, now weighing about two tons in all, swung out over the side of the lighter. It was carefully lowered until it was just below the surface of the water. George Hall then climbed down a rope ladder over the vessel's side, and together they descended eighty-four feet to the seabed. Once there, Hall felt his way around the bomb to make sure it had landed correctly against the wreck. It was important that it was actually touching the side of the wreck if it was to have its maximum effect. Everything was in order so Hall signalled to be hauled up to the surface. He climbed slowly back up the ladder and up the side of the lighter, having to lift over a hundredweight of lead and equipment with each step. Once on deck he stepped over to a small wooden bench where he sat to have his helmet and two forty-pound lead weights lifted off his chest. Hall gazed down at the water dripping from his suit making a puddle on the deck whilst he gasped to get his breath back. The Royal Engineer officer was standing impatiently in front of him waiting for his report. As soon as he could speak clearly, Hall reported that all was properly in place and the operation could proceed.

This pleased the officer who marched over to the large battery box, halted and stood to attention, ready to fire. All eyes turned to Pasley who was in his full ceremonial dress uniform, bristling with all his gleaming medals. He was standing proudly next to His Royal Highness the Duke of Cambridge in the middle of the group of dignitaries. Pasley purposefully took out his watch from his breast pocket and looked at it sternly. It was precisely 2 pm. Enjoying every moment of the attention, he strung it out as long as he dared. Eventually, he looked up, looked squarely in the eyes of the officer standing to attention at the battery, and gave a very slight solemn nod of his head. That was the signal the officer had been waiting for. He picked up a copper wire fitted with a brass termination, and with both hands, pressed it hard against a lead terminal on the battery.

The crowd fell silent. They held their breath and braced themselves for the massive explosion.

Nothing!

The electrical cable had somehow become disconnected and water had leaked into the gunpowder. It was a non-event. The crowds grumbled their disappointment as the word spread around the assembled fleet that the operation had been cancelled and one by one the boats gradually dispersed. An embarrassed Pasley made his apologies to His Royal Highness and other guests and dutifully saw them all off. He then quietly retreated to the privacy of his cabin on the *Success*. Nobody disturbed him. They knew it would not be a good time to discuss their personal problems. Pasley sat there pensively, cursing his bad luck and planning his next assault.

Over the next few weeks, smaller charges of between 45 and 180 pounds of gunpowder were successfully detonated. Once again the rehearsals for a spectacular explosion were planned optimistically. The next attempt was scheduled for Monday, 23rd September.

The morning of the 23rd saw thick fog shrouding the Solent. But by ten o'clock it had lifted and unveiled a beautiful day. The sea was as smooth as glass. To the slight dismay of Pasley, the assembled spectators did not include so many dignitaries this time, though he was honoured again with the presence of Lord Dundonald and Captain Basil Hall.

Another two-ton cylinder, this time containing 2,320 pounds of gunpowder was swung out and gently lowered to the seabed. George Hall once again ensured it was placed close alongside the hull, amidships, where the wreck was most compact. He carefully examined the connection of the conducting wires with the cylinder as best he could in the gloom and everything appeared in its proper place.

At two o'clock the surface vessels withdrew five hundred feet, the full distance the electrical wires between the charge and the voltaic battery would allow. At five minutes past two, as silence fell once more upon the crowd, Pasley, with watch in hand, nodded and the electrical circuit was closed.

Instantaneously everyone felt a severe shock through their feet accompanied by such a loud sound "as cannot be described". The surface of the sea above the wreck "became violently agitated into small irregular waves, a few inches only in height" over an area of about a hundred yards diameter. A few seconds later the water directly over the explosion suddenly leapt skywards to a height of about thirty feet forming a huge column the shape of a bee-hive as it rose and expanded upwards. When it fell back it caused "a circular wave of great beauty, being quite symmetrical, and about four feet high" which travelled outwards from its centre.

Pasley had at last achieved his big bang!

Nobody was left in any doubt that Colonel Pasley's attack on the *Royal George* was now in full swing. His explosion even rattled the windows in Portsea and the Dockyard.

Many more explosions, large and small, followed. Over the ensuing months a considerable amount of wood and artefacts was raised including twelve more guns, five gun carriages, and the galley, but nowhere near as much as Pasley had planned. He was also well behind in his estimation of the time needed to clear the wreck. His time ran out in November when the wintry weather eventually closed in. He was forced to call off his attack and retreat.

Throughout the 1839 season Pasley had been very pleased with the diving skills of George Hall and had grudgingly built up a deep respect for his services. He even described Hall as "the best diver in England". So at the end of the season, when Hall voiced his criticisms of the Sadler diving pumps and suggested to Pasley that he should consider obtaining the superior diving pump manufactured by Augustus Siebe, Pasley, to his credit, took the advice seriously. He would review his plans in preparation for his renewed campaign the following year. He was slowly coming round to the realisation that he had been wrong about the use of the diving bell and that he was going to be completely dependent on the helmet divers to win the campaign.

Following up Hall's suggestion, Pasley called in to see Siebe at 5 Denmark Street, Soho in London. It was in the heart of the engineering district of London though at the time it was not a particularly pleasant area.

Around the corner in the churchyard of St Giles the coffins were stacked up in piles because they arrived faster than they could be buried. Disease was rife. The rats that crawled all over them were some of the best fed in London. In fact, the rat population was doing so well that a sport had been invented specially for them. A poster outside the King's Head public house in nearby Compton Street invited punters to come in and enjoy "Ratting for the Million". A gold repeater watch was offered as a prize for the owner of the dog that could kill fifteen rats the fastest. To be fair, there were some strict rules. The dogs had to be under 13 3/4 pounds in weight and nobody was allowed to touch a dog or a rat once the match had started or the dog would be disqualified.

Siebe was in a different league from Sadler. Siebe was a

precision engineer. His workmanship was of the highest quality. He was a tall man and he stood with a straight back, much as his Prussian Army training had taught him. There was an aristocratic air about him and his face portrayed a sensitive intelligent man.

Pasley took to Siebe. They were like comrades in arms. They had a mutual respect for each other's abilities and accomplishments; perhaps also because they both had a military background and both had contributed to Napoleon's defeat as well as both having survived serious injuries inflicted by the warring French.

So Pasley then ordered one of Siebe's air pumps to be ready for the 1840 season on the *Royal George*. Over the winter, both Pasley and Siebe spent much of their time mulling over what they were going to do the following year.

As they did so, an important new player was preparing to enter the plot. A philanthropic gentleman and eminent civil engineer was waiting in the wings, poised to make his entrance.

He was to have a profound effect on Pasley, Siebe, the Deanes and the future of the diving helmet.

Part Three
Competition and Catastrophe

13
Open and close

In 1837 a prominent civil engineer named George Edwards had called in to Augustus Siebe at Denmark Street to buy a set of diving equipment. Siebe was by now was enjoying increasing sales of the Deane pattern open diving helmet. He was no longer tied to a commercial arrangement with Barnard because the so-called patent protection had run its fourteen years and lapsed in 1837. The diving helmet was now one of the major products in Siebe's sales catalogue.

Edwards was born of land-owning, religious stock of King's Lynn in Norfolk. He had turned down lucrative prospects as a member of the clergy in favour of his great passion for engineering. In this he had been trained by Joseph Cubitt, one of the best engineers in the country. He had spent several years in France designing railways, when, by 1837, he found himself as Superintendent of Lowestoft harbour.

The harbour had responsibility for several bridges and lock gates that were in desperate need of attention so he decided to use a Deane diving helmet to carry out underwater surveys. He was well acquainted with the option of the diving helmet because Charles Deane had previously carried out an underwater survey at the harbour for Joseph Cubitt in 1832.

Edwards had travelled to London in 1837 and bought a set of the Deane open helmet diving equipment from Siebe when he had been assured it was "the best that ever was". He went on to use it successfully himself at Lowestoft throughout that year. But he became exasperated by the tendency for the suit to fill with water if he leaned forward too far. The cold water spilled over the neck-entry of the suit and ran down his body. Not only was the feeling quite unpleasant but it made him very heavy when the time came to get out of the water. It was a little like climbing a ladder with wellingtons full of water, except this time the wellingtons came up to his ears. It also made him cold and reduced his endurance under the water. He thought it would make a big difference to the usefulness of the dress if this annoying problem could be avoided so he applied his resourceful brain and came up with a neat solution.

He concluded that the suit should be joined to the helmet with a watertight seal. Once that was done, no water would be able to enter the dress. He would be free to lean over as far as he wanted. He would even be able lie down in a horizontal position, which was impossible in an open helmet. In order to achieve the seal he needed, Edwards designed a loose flange which clamped the top edge of the waterproof diving dress tightly round the lower edge of the corselet, the part of the helmet which sat on the diver's shoulders and came down over the front of his chest and back. The brass straps which comprised the loose flange were conveniently clamped down by a series of wing-nuts and bolts.

The arrangement did however introduce a complication. Since no water could now enter the diving dress, there was nowhere for the air, which was being continuously pumped into the helmet, to escape. This was not as simple a problem to solve as it seemed. Clearly an exhaust valve had to be fitted somewhere for the air to escape, but the level where the air escaped from the dress was critical, as the Deanes had already discovered during their experiments in the Croydon Canal. If it was too low down, the dress inflated down to that level. This would cause over-inflation and the diver would bob to the surface like a balloon.

Edwards eventually designed a spring-loaded exhaust valve, which he fitted to the back of the helmet. The tension of the spring was carefully arranged to ensure that the air only escaped when it had reached the pressure of the water at the depth of the diver's chest. Once that pressure was achieved the force of the spring was overcome allowing the air to vent freely from the valve. Edwards added a spiral tube on the outside of the helmet, leading to the exhaust valve, to reduce the possibility of water leaking back into the helmet.

Having come up with this novel improvement, Edwards wrote to Siebe in 1838 and asked him if he would be prepared to build him a helmet to his specification. Siebe replied in September saying that he would be happy to oblige if Edwards would kindly send him the detailed construction drawings. After due consideration, Edwards decided it would be more practical for him to have his Deane helmet converted locally at Lowestoft.

The new helmet was ready the following year and on a sunny day in February he tested it in the harbour. He showed that he could lie down horizontally on the bottom, roll around and even allowed himself to be hauled to the surface feet first without the suit flooding and without any interruption to his air supply. It worked perfectly, and to distinguish it from the open helmet, Edwards called his version the "close helmet".

The crowds lining the quay wall were captivated by the demonstration as they had never seen anything like it before.

Edwards was understandably delighted with his conversion of the Deane open helmet. He went to London in June, taking his new helmet and dress with him to show it off to Siebe. He stayed overnight at Wood's Hotel, Furnival Inn, High Holborn, a convenient central point from where to launch his expeditions into the city. It was just a short walk to the Patent Office in Chancery Lane and to Siebe's manufactory in Denmark Street. By coincidence it was also close to John Bethell's office in Lincolns Inn Fields.

By yet another coincidence, Wood's Hotel was where a young reporter working for the *Morning Chronicle*, who had a burning ambition to become a popular novelist, had stayed between 1834 and 1837 and where he had started to write his first novel, *The Pickwick Papers*. He was, of course, Charles Dickens. He had then moved to a house round the corner in Doughty Street where he finished *The Pickwick Papers* and rattled off *Oliver Twist* and *Nicholas Nickleby*. The house remains in the Dickens family, which they retain as a museum and memorial to the great author.

George Edwards carefully unpacked his new diving helmet and dress in front of Siebe at Denmark Street. He was preparing himself for generous praise for his brilliant improvement but was taken aback when Siebe showed little interest. Siebe remained convinced that the Deane open helmet design was still "the best that ever was". Siebe was not, of course, a diver himself, so he was not in the best position to appreciate the operational merits of the Edwards conversion. Nevertheless, in an amazing act of altruism, Edwards told Siebe he was entirely free to adopt the design if he so wished. As far as he was concerned, his modifications made a significant contribution to the safety of the diving helmet and he did not wish to benefit commercially from it. Siebe politely acknowledged the generous offer but was non-committal in his response.

Edwards on the other hand was completely convinced that his modifications made a major improvement. So to make absolutely sure his close helmet design was placed conspicuously in the public domain, for all to see and use, he presented a paper on his "*Improvements in Diving Apparatus*" to a distinguished audience at the Institution of Civil

Engineers in George Street, near the Houses of Parliament, on 28th May 1839.

It was a superbly written paper. It described his modification to the Deane helmet in the fullest detail. He also used the opportunity to describe the principal competitive designs of diving helmets that had appeared since the introduction of the Deane diving helmet, including those of John Bethell, William Bush and John Fraser. To help illustrate his talk, Edwards placed his close helmet and dress on display at the Institution.

The paper was generally well received but there was one man in the audience who did not join in the approbation. In fact he was seething. That was the litigious John Bethell. He fanatically disapproved of a competitor enjoying so much acknowledgment and he objected energetically and viciously. Wielding his considerable influence, he stormed into the office of the secretary of the Institution and complained that Edwards's design infringed his patent. Raising his voice so that as many people as possible could hear him, he demanded that the close diving helmet on display be removed immediately.

Not wishing to be involved in any scandal, and perhaps in fear of losing his job, the browbeaten secretary complied. He apologised profusely to Edwards who was entirely sympathetic and understanding.

When Bethell's tirade eventually subsided, Edwards was able to determine that the only objection referred to the location of the exhaust valve being above the level of the diver's mouth, thus, according to Bethell, extracting the air "that was most vitiated". Bethell insisted this was a critical claim of his patent specification.

He raced over to the Affidavit Office in Chancery Lane and swore out an injunction against Edwards to prevent him from exhibiting or manufacturing his helmet design. On 4th June, the Vice-Chancellor's Court upheld the injunction. Bethell then strutted back to his office in Lincoln's Inn Fields and wrote a vicious and threatening letter to Edwards. He was proving to be a ruthless and bullying industrialist exploiting his privileged position as a practising lawyer.

Edwards patiently pointed out that Bethell's claim referred to an insignificant aspect of the design but to avoid unnecessary litigation he moved the position of the internal opening of the exhaust valve a couple of inches lower on the helmet. This avoided any conflict with Bethell's alleged patent rights but had no consequence whatsoever in the performance of the helmet. Bethell's objection evaporated into thin air. He was unable to find any further objection and the whole fuss fizzled away to thin air.

Bethell eventually found fame and fortune following his patenting of creosote which he had registered in 1838. This obnoxious mixture of poisonous chemical compounds quickly became heavily used as a wood preservative and Bethell established several factories around London to manufacture it. How a lawyer-cum-patent agent sitting in Lincolns Inn Fields came to 'invent' creosote is difficult to imagine. A sceptical person might conclude that an unscrupulous and greedy patent lawyer acquired the idea from a swindled inventor.

Whatever the background, the burgeoning diving industry was well rid of Bethell. He had turned out to be an obnoxious mixture of poisonous compounds himself and been nothing but a liability to the industry.

George Edwards went on to have a very successful career as a marine civil engineer. He worked with some of the best engineers in the country including Sir William Cubitt and Sir Samuel Peto. He was made the Justice of the Peace for the County of Suffolk and frequently attended the Lowestoft Bench. His philanthropic activities included donating land to the church at Oulton and building a coffee house for the poor and the seaman's mission at Lowestoft. He lived to the ripe old age of 89 years. He had chosen his own memorial stone for his grave which was an Ice Age granite boulder he had bumped into whilst strolling around the bottom of Lowestoft harbour. It will outlast every other gravestone in Oulton Churchyard by thousands of years.

For Colonel Pasley and his men, the 1840 campaign on the *Royal George* got off to a good start. On Thursday, 1st May, there was another massive explosion on the wreck. Nobody in Portsmouth could have been left in any doubt that Pasley was back in town. He had restructured his battle plan over the winter and one of the changes for the second year of operations was that the Whitstable divers should train some of his own men in the use of the diving helmet.

He had been corresponding with Siebe about procuring additional diving equipment and they had even discussed the possibility of trying a close helmet. But the ever-frugal Pasley had ordered that the new diving dress should be bought only if it was "absolutely necessary". Siebe had been more impressed with the Edwards conversion of the Deane diving helmet than he had initially let on. He had developed his own version of Edwards's loose flange over the winter months and had speculatively manufactured an example of the new close helmet and dress.

Pasley made one of his big decisions on 4th May. After exhaustive research, painstaking consideration and taking all relevant factors into account, he ordered a new set of diving equipment from Siebe via the Lords Commissioners of the Admiralty. The new equipment arrived in Portsmouth on 26th June. It was the first time Siebe had supplied a diving helmet to the military and it turned out to be a close diving helmet, incorporating George Edwards's novel loose flange.

It was a truly seminal event.

George Hall was the first diver to try it out. He had originally been taught to dive by John Deane himself and he was a dyed-in-the-wool open helmet advocate. Diving in a close helmet didn't come naturally to him and he was highly sceptical about its merits. He was not looking forward to trying it at all. But he had to do it because that was what Pasley wanted.

Hall sat patiently as he was dressed into the new equipment. The long length of time it was taking to tighten up all the bolts around the helmet was disconcerting. He felt trapped inside the dress. It didn't feel right to be completely sealed inside a helmet, just like in a coffin. He had never felt claustrophobic before, but now he was beginning to find out what it was like. The noise made by the spanner accidentally striking the side of the helmet as the wing nuts were being tightened was deafening. It was like having one's head inside a church bell when it was struck.

Finally everything was ready and he descended the rope ladder to the *Royal George*. Once he was in the water he was relieved to discover he felt much better. In fact it felt almost the same as in the open helmet. Initially, he was overly cautious and moved about on the wreck very warily. But he gained confidence quickly and was particularly pleased with his newfound ability to be able to lean forward as far as he liked and to be able to handle debris at his feet without any cold seawater running down his neck. He was soon leaping around the wreck as he had never done before. The close helmet was a definite improvement and Hall was an instant convert.

Hall reported back to Pasley that the new diving dress met with his approval and Pasley patted himself on the back for having made a good decision. If that didn't convince Pasley that the close helmet represented the shape of things to come, then Private Andrew Duncan of the Royal Sappers and Miners made sure it was.

Duncan was one of Pasley's best men and he had been trained to dive by George Hall. On this particular day, he had been groping around on the wreck in an open helmet when he had lost his footing and fallen forward. Inevitably his helmet flooded completely. He managed to give the emergency signal on his lifeline and alert the surface party did their best to haul him up as quickly as possible but he was unconscious by the time he arrived. Fortunately, after having his helmet removed he recovered consciousness quickly and made a full recovery. It had been a close call.

But the lesson had been learnt. Falling over in an open helmet could very likely end in fatal consequences, whilst a diver suffering the same fall in a close helmet would not be placed in any danger whatsoever. As far as Pasley was concerned, if he ever bought another helmet, it would be a close helmet. Siebe's future prosperity was assured. He had established himself as the favoured diving equipment manufacturer with the Royal Engineers. If only sliced bread had been invented by that time, Siebe was the best thing since it had been, as far as Pasley was concerned.

Pasley's operations on the *Royal George* were the equivalent of today's front-page news. The newspapers all over the country were clamouring for news of the latest developments. Pasley cleverly took full advantage of their appetite and wrote column after column of editorial. His prolific words were reported in *The Times* and just about every other major newspaper in the country. The coverage of the continuing saga even spread across the Atlantic to America and elsewhere. Pasley was becoming an international celebrity. Never before had he enjoyed so much attention and he was revelling in every moment of it.

In September 1840, the *Hampshire Telegraph* reported on a

visit by the Lords Commissioners of the Admiralty to the *Royal George* operations. They went out from Portsmouth harbour in the *Firebrand* steamer and toured the salvage operations at Spithead.

Naturally, a large explosion was arranged to take place during the visit.

The gunpowder charge had been taken down by Corporal Harris, another of Pasley's excellent men who had recently been trained to dive by the Whitstable divers. He had become so proficient in the use of Siebe's diving dress that, as a party-piece, he would descend headfirst. The Lords of the Admiralty enthusiastically observed the new Siebe diving equipment and the proceedings were all faithfully reported in the *Hampshire Telegraph*. In the same article, Pasley pointed out the various advantages that the Siebe close helmet had over the Deane open helmet.

Unfortunately, John Deane saw the article. It was like a red rag to a bull. The integrity of the Deane open helmet had been challenged. Pasley had thrown down his gauntlet. John, who was normally a very restrained man, had to fight to control his anger. He was not at all intimidated by Pasley and he was more than ready to face up to him, regardless of his military rank.

There was only one thing for it. He had to retaliate with an article of his own. This time the merits of the open helmet would be more fully and fairly described. John wrote his retaliatory letter and dropped it into the *Hampshire Telegraph* office in the High Street, Portsea. The *Telegraph* didn't have the nerve to become embroiled in a dispute involving Pasley and refused to print John's repost. But they did offer to do so if John removed "six lines of his communication".

John, of course, refused. These were very important lines. There was a principle at stake.

John was not to be defeated. He had one more option left open to him. There was another local newspaper, a direct competitor to the *Hampshire Telegraph* and this was the *Hampshire Independent*. True to its name, the *Independent* did not flinch from publishing John's opinion in full, and at the same time point out the lack of back-bone of the *Telegraph*. John was thus able to return Pasley's fire robustly and he met him in a head-on confrontation.

Only a very brave or very foolish man would normally stand his ground against Pasley.

On 3rd October, John was able to report in the *Independent* that he had used his open helmet for the last twelve years. He had been down as long as five hours and forty minutes in one dive alone, and as deep as one hundred and forty feet. Referring to a salvage operation he had carried out on the wreck of the *Lady Charlotte* on the south coast of Ireland the previous year, he stated he had recovered £96,000 in specie for Lloyds underwriters. He said that divers had to lie down horizontally to reach the treasure in deep cavities in the rocks, though John was perhaps stretching the truth a little with this claim. He claimed that not one life had been lost by a diver using his equipment, though the lives of four divers had already been sacrificed in the so-called "improved apparatus".

When his letter was published, John braced himself, expecting all Hell to break loose as soon as Pasley saw it.

But the counter offensive never came. Surprisingly, Pasley didn't respond to any aspect of the article and the correspondence simply came to an abrupt halt. It is to John's credit that Pasley withdrew quietly from the field of public battle but it was completely out of character for him, after all, he had at one time written in his diary when involved with an unrelated confrontation "I determine to revert to my first principle of NO COMPROMISE, NO SURRENDER". The block capitals were his. Pasley just wasn't the surrendering type.

The only explanation for Pasley's retreat can be that he felt unsure of a victory. John was not going to be an easy push over. He could not pull military rank over civilians. It would be man to man. He was not on safe ground outside the walls of a military establishment and he could sense that John held the moral high ground. Neither would it do his career any good to become involved in a personal and very public fight.

John may have won the battle, but what about the war? It looked like a tactical withdrawal on the surface, but Pasley had a long memory. As far as he was concerned, a day would come when he would exact his revenge, no doubt when John was least expecting it. John would need to watch his back.

Pasley did not of course change his mind about the merits of the Siebe helmet. In fact he went ahead and ordered another set of the close dress from Siebe. The Royal Engineers deserved the best. And anyway, Pasley was slipping behind schedule and he needed to speed up the operation if he was to keep his high profile reputation intact.

The ongoing coverage of the *Royal George* operations in the nation's newspapers continued to amuse the public and generate much debate. It attracted the attention of writers like Charles Dickens, himself a native of Portsmouth. In his article entitled *Mechanics in Uniform*, Dickens described the work of the Royal Sappers and Miners. He wrote how on one occasion, Corporal Jones came upon Corporal Skelton whilst working on the wreck and he could hear Skelton singing a song to himself inside his Siebe helmet. Dickens went on to make many more references to helmet divers and their work throughout his career, even visiting Whitstable to research the new diving industry being fostered there.

The national publicity that the diving operations in the Solent was receiving gave John an idea for a special publication. The cannons and many other fascinating artefacts which he had recovered, not only from the *Mary Rose* and the *Royal George* but from a host of other wrecks he had dived on, were a great novelty and of considerable historic interest. So he decided to produce a prestige document to illustrate his finds in full colour, which he called his "*Cabinet of Submarine Recoveries*". He established a list of twenty-two eminent subscribers to ensure the costs would be covered, which included Lords, Admirals, Knights, Earls, Captains, Honourables, Reverends and other dignitaries who had an interest in the famous wrecks. Colonel Pasley's name was notably absent. John next commissioned a popular Portsmouth artist named Henry Ubsdell to paint accurate pictures of the trophies that lay around his house. Ubsdell also visited the dockyard with John several times to paint the ornate cannons, which John had recently recovered from the *Mary Rose* and were still being carefully guarded at the Gunwharf. On one of his visits to the Gunwharf with Ubsdell, John caught another artist making an 'unauthorised' sketch of one of his *Mary Rose* cannons. John immediately threw him out and promptly arranged with the dockyard to ban any further unofficial artists from viewing the cannons. He had to protect his own publication.

John put together a fine collection of these valuable illustrations ready to publish in his Cabinet. But when it came to the crunch, not enough of the original sponsors came up with their funding so John unfortunately never completed his project. The paintings ended up adorning the walls of his home in Gosport. Today these elegant pictures provide an accurate and priceless record of the artefacts that he had recovered and they now reside in the vaults of Portsmouth City Archives and are brought out only occasionally for special exhibitions.

The well-publicised *Mary Rose* diving operations attracted the attention of a quixotic character named Tom Steele. He came from a background of landed gentry in County Clare, Ireland and had been educated at Cambridge University. He had been interested in the art of diving for many years and had even taken out a patent for a unique design of diving bell. When Charles Deane had been diving on the wreck of the *Intrinsic* at Kilkee in County Clare, back in 1836, Steele had met up with him and provided him with a great deal of local support. In return, Charles had allowed Steel the great privilege of a dive in his helmet equipment. Steele subsequently became an enthusiastic supporter of the Deane diving dress. Having read about the *Mary Rose* diving operations, he turned up at John's house in Gosport eloquently requesting to dive on the wreck himself. He was a delightful character and though in his fifties, John was easily persuaded to let him have a dive.

Tom Steele had an amazing background. Having inherited an enormous estate in County Clare from an uncle about twenty years previously, he almost bankrupted himself immediately in an abortive military adventure in the Spanish Civil War when he attempted to assist the Constitutionalists against the Royalists. He bought a large consignment of arms, ammunition and military equipment and placed the whole consignment aboard a brig in London. He set sail for Spain with his precious cargo and first arrived in Vigo, from where he was hurriedly sent on his way again by a strong contingent of Royalists. He was forced to continue his voyage around the coast of Spain, all the way to Gibraltar because all his attempts to land the military stores were foiled by the military successes of the Royalists and their French allies. Ultimately, all the stores were captured by the Royalists and the expedition turned into a catastrophic failure. He had ended up unwittingly sponsoring his enemy. Steele never recovered from this financial setback, though it never curbed his inborn enthusiasm.

Steele went on to become heavily involved in Irish politics. As a Protestant, he fought selflessly for the Emancipation of Catholics and assumed the responsibility of ensuring that Daniel O'Connell's cause was fought without violence. He became one of O'Connell's most trusted companions who bestowed on him the grand title of no less than "The Head Pacificator For Ireland". He was a tall, broad-shouldered and well-built man so his mere presence tended to subdue any thoughts of violence. This was a man of the very highest moral principles and he was prepared to die for them. Indeed his absolute commitment to honesty and fairness earned him the nickname of "Honest Tom Steele".

One of his political adventures included the abduction of the "Seffin Stone" from Birr in County Offaly. The stone holds enormous cultural significance to the Irish and is known as the "Navel of Ireland", supposedly marking the centre of Ireland. It is said to have been used as a mass rock, when the Catholic religion was suppressed and religious ceremonies were held in the open air.

It took two days of hard labour to detach the stone from its bed. It weighed several tons and it took six horses and fifty men with ropes and hand spikes to get it moving. A carriage, canal boat, another carriage and several public speeches eventually succeeded in bringing the stone to his home at Kilkee. It was only returned to Birr as recently as 1974.

On another occasion Steele duelled with pistols to defend O'Connell's honour, though both duellists thankfully missed their targets, but duly retained their honour.

The good work of divers, both military and civilian, was receiving ever-increasing acknowledgment in the newspapers. Their numbers were growing steadily and everything seemed to be progressing well for the emerging diving profession.

But there was an insidious problem festering amongst the divers that threatened to undermine the healthy growth of the new industry.

Few people were aware of it and the divers themselves tried to ignore it. They were reluctant to talk about it. There was a strong element of denial about it. Indeed, the denial aspect became part of the problem. It only became apparent when it reached an intolerable level. There would be no chance of solving this problem if the divers didn't admit to it.

The problem was "the pain".

14
THE PAIN

There was nothing unusual about the aches and pains associated with hard physical work, but the divers on the *Royal George* operations were suffering from more than their fair share of them. It was all rather mysterious.

Pasley had noted that Corporal Harris suffered terribly from "rheumatism". Sometimes he recorded that Harris was simply "ill". George Hall, the principal Whitstable diver who was arguably one of the most highly motivated helmet divers in the country, was in so much pain that he had to leave the site and return home "on account of an illness". On one occasion, a naval doctor from nearby Haslar Hospital visited the diving operation and he noted that after the divers had surfaced, he frequently saw them leaning against the side of the hulk, pale, languid and exhausted.

Rheumatism became such a common and acute problem that the Royal Engineers introduced special measures to combat it. Each diver was to be well clothed in flannel or woollen dresses. They were advised to wear two under-suits at a time, each consisting of a pair of drawers, stockings, and a woollen Guernsey frock. After each dive these were to be taken off and thoroughly dried and aired. A constant change was necessary, so each diver was allocated six under-suits.

At the *Royal George* operations, a special drying room was set aside on the vessel on which the divers were quartered. It had a stove in the centre and rails all around for hanging the dresses. The divers' attendants would bring the used dresses to the drying room immediately after the diver surfaced and take him a fresh dry set for the next dive. Despite these elaborate arrangements, the divers were still "subject to violent attacks of rheumatism".

If it wasn't the pain of rheumatism, it was another strange condition which Pasley initially described as "over fatigue". It would affect the more zealous of the divers, regardless of their considerable physical strength. Indeed, Pasley attributed the problem to over-exertion. The affected diver would simply fall to the floor when back on deck and be unable to get up again, even when ordered to do so. At one time, Pasley even used the words "a sort of paralysis" to describe the condition.

In any event, the problem either went away of its own accord, perhaps after a few days in the naval hospital at Haslar, or if not, by replacing the crippled diver with a fresh one.

It was to take another twenty years or so before these mystifying illnesses were identified as being caused by bubbles forming in the divers' body tissues after they had surfaced and subsequently dubbed the "bends". The strange term was derived from the way that the divers bent their affected limbs when suffering from the crippling pain.

Playing with explosives on the seabed was also opening up new opportunities and simultaneously introducing new problems.

John Deane had recommenced his exploration of the wreck of the *Mary Rose* in 1840, this time with thirteen-inch, explosive mortar shells detonated by voltaic battery. By this crude but effective excavation technique, he was able to unearth more artefacts buried deep inside the remains of the ship's hull. The biggest piece he recovered was the bottom fifteen feet of the ship's main mast, which was a massive piece of timber.

In all, John salvaged four magnificent bronze cannons, a large number of breach-loading wrought iron cannons, iron, lead and granite shot, a match lock gun, long bows, brass sheaves, a curious padlock, an anchor, a pump, human skulls and bones, and various pieces of oak timber.

He had amassed so much, that he held a profitable public auction at The Point, Portsmouth, on 12th November 1840. The section of the mainmast alone fetched £30. The Ordnance paid John handsomely for the bronze guns, one fetching over £220 (over £15,000 in today's money). Two of these are now displayed at the *Mary Rose* museum at Portsmouth and the other two are in the Tower of London.

But all John could do was to scratch the surface. In due course the flow of artefacts started to run out and he eventually had to look elsewhere for alternative diving projects.

Little did he know that more than half of the ancient ship's hull and most of the ship's contents lay buried under the mud, hidden from view. It was not until recent times that the ship was rediscovered by the late Alexander McKee and raised under the personal patronage of His Royal Highness Prince Charles. It is now on display in Portsmouth Dockyard alongside HMS *Victory*. A new museum building is presently being prepared to show off this magnificent Tudor warship with a budget of £35m.

Throughout 1840 there had been a diving triangle in the Solent. Pasley's divers were clearing away the *Royal George*, Henry Abbinett was breaking up the *Boyne* whilst John was working on the *Mary Rose*. All three kept a keen eye on each other, not least because they were all experimenting with exploding gunpowder under water using the voltaic battery and they were all doing it in close collaboration with Portsmouth Dockyard. John Deane was probably the most proficient, followed closely by Pasley, with Abbinett some way behind in third place. Despite the occasional competitive clash between John and Abbinett, they remained good friends and actually worked together on a variety of wreck salvage projects over the ensuing years.

In June, Abbinett placed a 300-pound gunpowder charge on the wreck of the *Boyne*. The Royal Navy were glad of the opportunity to rid itself of an obstruction very near to the entrance to Portsmouth Harbour so they had built the large explosive charge especially for him in the Dockyard. Pasley also contributed by lending Sergeant-Major Jones and one of his voltaic batteries to detonate the charge. After Abbinett had placed the charge he climbed back into his boat where Jones was preparing the battery under Pasley's watchful eye. The planned explosion, which was going to be only a few hundred yards off the beach at Southsea, naturally drew a large crowd. At the appointed hour the electrical circuit was closed and the result was eagerly awaited.

As occasionally happened, the charge failed to fire.

John Deane happened to be in his boat amongst the fleet of curious craft hovering around the planned spectacle. When he realised that Abbinett's charge had failed he sailed up alongside Abbinett's boat and offered his services. Pasley did not immediately take to the idea of John getting involved with his exploding apparatus. But he could see that this was going to be the only option he had to resolve the immediate problem. And with so many people watching he could hardly refuse. So he reluctantly gave his permission.

John dived and replaced two charges in quick succession "with great skill and precision". Then, on both occasions, when Sergeant-Major Jones applied his voltaic battery there were very satisfying explosions.

In a perfect world, John and Pasley might have been able to

settle their differences at their meeting over the *Boyne*. But that would mean that Pasley would have had to admit he had been wrong about John. Sadly, the chance of that happening was remote. Pasley was neither the forgiving nor compromising type. In his blinkered military mind, John was for some inexplicable reason, squarely in the enemy camp. Regardless of whatever John did to try and appease Pasley, it was always going to be interpreted as an underhand hostile manoeuvre.

It just so happened, that when one of the explosions went off on the *Boyne*, George Hall was working underwater on the *Royal George* about a mile away. It nearly caused him a serious accident. The underwater shockwave hit him hard and he later said that it felt as if something large and heavy had been dropped on his helmet.

The incident came as a complete surprise.

No such trauma was caused to people above the surface of the water who were much closer to the explosion. A new physical principle had been discovered. Pressure waves were transmitted more efficiently through water than through air. The lesson was soon to be reinforced when an even closer shave befell Private John Skelton. He had been down on the *Royal George* and had placed a charge of just sixty pounds of gunpowder. Due to some misunderstanding on the surface, the charge was detonated before Skelton had left the water. In fact he was still a few feet below the surface when it went off.

Skelton was actually knocked unconscious by the shock he received. He was hauled back to the surface and he appeared to recover quickly apart from a severe pain in his chest. Skelton therefore had the dubious honour of being the first recorded casualty of an underwater explosion. As a precaution, Skelton was sent to Haslar Hospital where leeches were immediately applied to his chest. Unfortunately the cure didn't work and he never dived again, although he was kept on to assist the diving teams on the surface. Skelton's luck finally ran out in 1844 when he fell overboard from a boat at Spithead and drowned.

There were also some additional problems that were directly attributable to the diving activity and specifically to Siebe's new close helmet. A couple of these came under the generic heading of "the squeeze".

First, if a diver made a sudden, accidental descent whilst under water, such as falling from one deck to a lower one on a wreck, or to the seabed, he suffered a squeeze. This was because he made a sudden transition from the water pressure at one depth to the greater pressure at a deeper depth. If this was carried out slowly, in a controlled manner, there was no problem as the attendants working the diver's air pump could increase the pressure within the diver's suit by continued pumping. But if the change in depth and pressure happened quickly the air pressure inside the suit could not be increased quickly enough.

The painful result meant the flexible dress pressed hard onto the diver. The pressure was so great that it immediately prevented the diver from breathing. The forces of nature next tried to squeeze the diver up into his helmet.

But divers into helmets won't go, arithmetically speaking.

So nature then squeezes the bit that will go. To all intents and purposes, this means the diver's blood was squashed from the diver's body into his head and neck. Unfortunately, the diver's head and neck cannot comfortably accommodate the large volume of blood coming up from his body, so it swells. Sordid descriptions refer variously to the diver's eyes popping out, his head and neck swelling up like a balloon as they filled with blood. In the more grotesque cases it had proven difficult to remove the helmet from the diver's head because it had swollen to such a size it filled the inside of the helmet.

One graphic description was written in 1854 when an English diver named Tope was diving on a wreck in the USA:

"The signal line was at once worked to ascertain if anything was wrong; but receiving no answer, they at once drew him to the surface, and on opening the armour, to their horror, found him quite dead; although he had been down but one minute. The corpse presented such a dreadful spectacle; blood was oozing from the eyes, nose and mouth ... we found the head very badly swollen, the face and neck so filled with blood as to resemble liver, while the rest of the body was as white as unclouded marble."

Happily, this horrifying condition was restricted to the close helmet. It could not befall a diver wearing an open helmet because all that would happen to him is that the water level in the helmet would rise to the top and the diver would have felt no squeeze at all. Of course this would have been small comfort because he would not have been able to breathe and drowning would have been a fast-approaching problem.

At least the diver in the open helmet had the luxury of then having some alternative options from which to choose. He could wait for the water level in his helmet to descend once more as the surface pump caught up with the increase in pressure, or he could climb up his life line or air line to return to the shallower depth, or simply give an emergency signal on his life line and hope that the attendant on the surface hauled him up to shallower water quickly enough.

The second possible cause of a squeeze happened if the diver's air pipe burst. If this disastrous event did happen to a diver, the usual place the air pipe would rupture was at or near the surface, because that is where the greatest difference occurred between the pressure inside the pipe and the pressure outside. Deeper down in the water the inside and outside pressures were closer together, so there was less risk of the pipe bursting there.

The pipe leading down to the diver didn't collapse because its wall was reinforced with a spiral wire, intentionally to keep it open and prevent it from kinking. So the next thing that happened was that the pressurised air inside the diver's dress on the bottom escaped to the surface through his open air pipe. The result was a rapid, catastrophic drop in the pressure in the diver's dress, and mother nature once again tried to force the diver into his helmet and up his air line.

On these occasions, the squeezing pressure on the diver was so great, and it happened so rapidly that by the time he was hauled to the surface, the damage was done. The squashed diver was usually dead on arrival. But if he was lucky enough to survive the squeeze, the standard treatment at the hospital was the application of leeches to his swollen neck, and a turpentine enema, perhaps giving rise to the term "adding insult to injury".

There were two separate incidents of the burst air hose and squeeze during the *Royal George* operations. The unlucky casualties were Private Roderick Cameron and Private John Williams.

In both cases, their air pipes burst at the surface, near their air pumps. When they burst, there was a very loud 'bang' followed by a hissing noise as the diver's air escaped from the ruptured end which was flailing crazily around on the deck like a convulsing snake. The surface attendants had a big shock when it happened as it sounded much like the crack of a gun going off. But at least they realised immediately what had happened. Thanks to the rapid response of the surface attendants, in both cases, the divers were recovered to the surface so quickly that they survived, just. After Cameron recovered in Haslar Hospital, he reported that the "first sensation was that of suffocation". He then had a feeling of being crushed before he lost consciousness.

Again, if an open helmet diver's air pipe burst, all that occurred was that water rushed into his helmet and up his air line. So a rapid return to the surface would have become high on the diver's list of priorities.

The good news was that the problem of the burst air pipe had a simple and effective remedy. Pasley arranged for a non-return valve to be fitted into the air inlet connection at the back of the diving helmet. This ensured that in the event of loss of pressure in the air pipe, the valve would close automatically and seal off the helmet. The pressure in the diving dress would thus be prevented from falling.

This did not however, solve the associated problem of the loss of the diver's air supply. The diver was expected to rely on breathing the small volume of air trapped inside the helmet and dress until he reached the surface. So at least he had a few minutes to extricate himself from his dilemma.

Pasley also addressed the problem of the overheating of the air pumps. The strange phenomenon was noticed when the divers went particularly deep. The compression of the air in the cylinders inside the pump caused the air to heat up. The deeper the diver, the greater the pressure, the hotter it got. It could get so hot it could burn fingers. This had several detrimental effects. First it caused the pump's lubricating oils to break down and produced an unpleasant and unhealthy smell in the diver's breathing air. Second, when the hot air became cooled as it travelled down the air hose to the diver, its volume was reduced thus reducing the efficiency of the pump. Third, the heat was weakening the hose material itself and making it more likely to burst under pressure. Clearly something had to be done about it. So Pasley introduced a water jacket around the cylinders to help keep them cool. This improvement made a big difference for the comfort and safety of the diver.

The injuries on the *Royal George* operations were not all confined to medical conditions or equipment failure.

An underwater first was achieved in 1842 when Lance-Corporal Jones and Private Girvan were working on the wreck. Each of the two divers was operating from a separate hulk at the surface and each had been allocated a separate section of the wreck on which to work. They were in the process of recovering timbers that had been broken from the hull by previous explosions. Inevitably, the process developed into a competition between the divers operating from the two hulks. The more timber that was sent up, the greater was the skill and reputation of the diver.

The system worked well, until 22nd September.

In the poor visibility, both divers began working unwittingly at opposite ends of the same piece of timber. As they progressed along the timber to make sure it was clear, they suddenly bumped into each other near the middle and a scuffle ensued. Each of the divers tried to claim the timber for himself.

The diligent attendants on the surface could feel repetitive jerks on the divers' life lines and air lines as the two divers fought each other. They naturally assumed the divers were in some sort of trouble so they began to haul them to the surface. Jones's attendants took an early lead and initially pulled him up a little higher than Girvan. When Girvan saw Jones disappearing upwards he grabbed one of his legs to prevent his escape. Jones felt Girvan's grasp on his leg and swung round with his free leg to dislodge him. Jones's heavy boot went straight into the faceplate of Girvan's helmet, shattering the glass.

Girvan's helmet and suit immediately filled with water, so he released Jones's leg.

It took a whole three minutes to get Girvan back up to the surface by which time he was already unconscious. It took four men to haul his heavy body with all the attached lead weights, helmet and a suit full of water up the side of the hulk and onto the deck. But thankfully he was still alive. He was sent immediately to the hospital at Haslar where he was eventually nursed back to health, no doubt with the assistance of a few hungry leeches and liberal turpentine enemas. The divers on the *Royal George* were making heavy demands on the nation's supply of leeches and turpentine. Hopefully they were not being recycled.

Girvan was understandably very unhappy with Jones and threatened to take action against him in a civil court. Pasley didn't like to see dissention in the ranks and intervened. He patiently listened to the individual accounts of the incident from Girvan and Jones. After due consideration he judged that both were equally to blame so he persuaded Girvan to drop the action. It was not long before the two divers were the best of friends again. Girvan and Jones also had the satisfaction of knowing that they had entered the record books for the first instance of single combat between two divers at the bottom of the sea.

During the second season on the *Royal George*, Pasley had got George Hall to train six of his own men. This enabled him to dispense with the services of Hall and the other two Whitstable divers and save some money. Despite his high opinion of Hall, he was pleased that he no longer had to pay civilians to carry out the clearance work. He was also pleased with himself for having introduced an important new skill to the Royal Engineers.

Pasley had originally promised the Admiralty that he would have returned the anchorage at Spithead to them clear of the wreck of the *Royal George,* before the end of 1840. But he had only made a small dent in it by the end of the season. He had seriously underestimated the task. The cycles of explosions, followed by the painstakingly slow recovery of sections of timber by the divers, dragged on through 1841, 1842 and 1843. But at least by then, Pasley had established a group of hardened, expert divers within his ranks.

Virtually all the remaining guns had been recovered. In fact, they now had so many bronze guns from the *Royal George* they didn't know what to do with them all. One of the options that had been put forward by the late King William IV to form a battery of the guns at Windsor Castle had not survived the change in the monarchy in 1837, when Queen Victoria had come to the throne. The issue became a matter of popular political debate.

In 1842, the building of Nelson's 145-foot column in Trafalgar Square was completed. The bronze capital and granite statue of Admiral Nelson were due to be placed on the top in 1843. The brilliant suggestion was then made that the guns could be melted down and recast to form the

Corinthian capital for the column. And that is where the thirty or so of Pasley's *Royal George* bronze cannons ended up.

All of them except, that is, for a couple that Pasley held back as memorials to his epic *Royal George* clearance enterprise. He had always been a little envious of the fact that Charles Deane had had his name immortalised on a plaque placed on a bronze *Royal George* cannon in 1834 which was on public display in Portsmouth. Today, this gun is displayed in Southsea Castle. So Pasley hounded the Board of Ordnance until, finally, in 1849, they presented him with a bronze, *Royal George*, 24-pounder mounted on a gun carriage made from wood recovered from the wreck and carrying plaques on either side commemorating the clearance campaign.

By 1843, Pasley had been promoted to Major-General in recognition of his quite considerable services to the country. His authority had never been greater. So when he wrote to the Board of the Admiralty in July 1843 with a constructive suggestion they were duty bound to sit up and pay attention.

Pasley's suggestion was that "it will be of great advantage to the service of the Royal Navy to have men qualified to act as Divers in every fleet". The Navy already had a policy to equip every flagship with a diving apparatus, but perversely they had no policy to ensure there were men on board trained in its use.

Pasley further suggested that he be allowed to train suitable naval volunteers to dive during his last few months of clearance operations on the *Royal George* site. Most controversially of all, he proposed that Sir Thomas Hastings, Captain of the gunnery school on board HMS *Excellent* permanently moored in Portsmouth harbour, be ordered to commence the training of young officers or mates or volunteer seamen as divers and submarine miners.

Pasley was attempting to do with one letter, what the Deanes had been trying to achieve for more than ten years. The Admiralty simply was not used to adopting new ideas that quickly. But coming from a Major-General, the suggestion carried a little more weight. With uncharacteristic speed, the Admiralty agreed to Pasley's suggestion and instructed him to co-ordinate with Sir Thomas Hastings at Portsmouth to put his proposals into effect. Sir Thomas however, was not so keen. He was not happy with outsiders coming in and telling him how to run his own ship. Pasley was rocking his boat.

Sir Thomas made various excuses and stalled Pasley's plan. Needless to say, Pasley responded with his biggest diplomatic guns firing.

He wrote to Admiral Sir George Cockburn of the Admiralty stating that Sir Thomas was "very jealous about this measure" and that he was dragging his heels. Admiral Cockburn was not amused. He was also a man of action. He had commanded the detachment of Royal Marines that had set the city of Washington ablaze during the brief Anglo-American war of 1812. He had also been the Commander of HMS *Northumberland* when he transported the defeated Napoleon Bonaparte to his terminal exile on the island of St Helena.

Pasley's letter to Cockburn had immediate effect. The Admiralty ordered Sir Thomas to comply.

Sir Thomas complied. It was either that or face a firing squad.

Thirteen volunteer petty officers and seamen from HMS *Excellent* promptly reported for duty at the *Royal George* operations in September 1843. But virtually nothing remained of the *Royal George* for them to clear by then so Pasley's men moved their diving operations to the wreck of HMS *Edgar*, about half a mile to the east. The *Edgar* had been a 3rd rate man-of-war of 74 guns, which had caught fire and exploded whilst at anchor in 1711. So the first class of Navy divers cut their teeth on the wreck of HMS *Edgar* in eighty-five feet of water at Spithead.

HMS *Excellent* thus became the first and principal Royal Naval diving school. In 1891 the ship was transferred ashore to nearby Whale Island, becoming the first naval training ship to become a shore establishment, or "stone frigate". It has remained there ever since.

Both John and Charles Deane felt a little pride when they heard of the establishment of the naval diving school at Portsmouth. Their invention of the diving helmet had at last made a major impact and become an acknowledged asset for their country.

But what about personal recognition and perhaps even remuneration?

15
Up and down

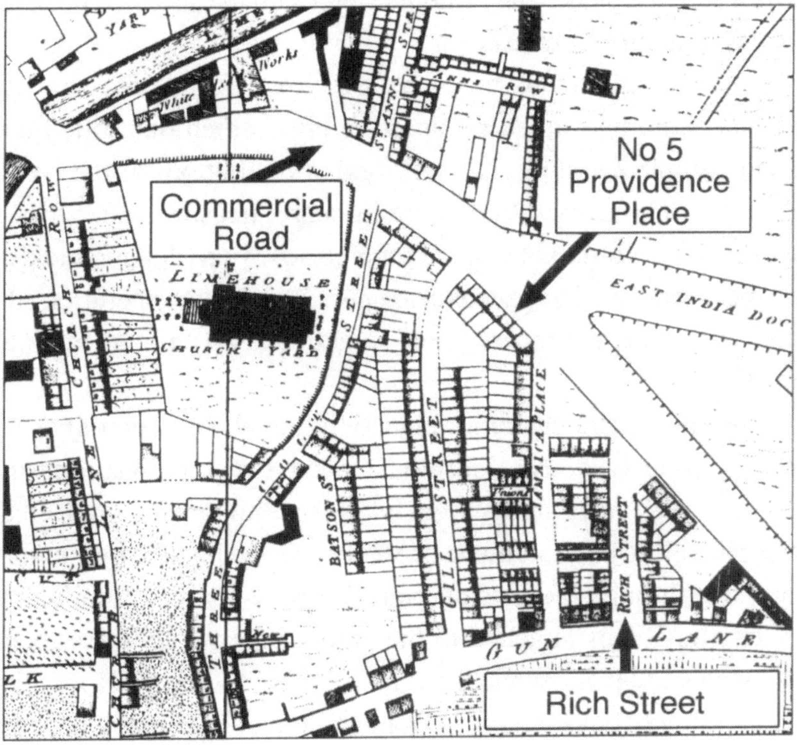

The lives of John and Charles Deane were developing in different directions by 1843.

John had become a successful full-time professional diver in partnership with William Edwards of Whitstable. He was an acknowledged expert in the use of explosives under water and their electrical detonation. He had moved to Gosport, near Portsmouth, and he had his own very seaworthy boat.

The year started off well for him when he was invited to France to solve a riddle that had been perplexing the French for over fifty years. A mystery surrounded a wreck called the *Telemaque* sunk near Quillebeuf in the river Seine. She had been in a group of ships commissioned by French noblemen and their families in a desperate attempt to avoid the guillotine and escape to England during the French revolution in 1790. But her luck had run out and she was caught in a storm. She grounded in shallow water and sank. The rumours suggested the ship had been loaded with a vast quantity of treasure.

Every attempt to raise the wreck or to get into the hold to salvage its cargo had failed because the hull, which had rolled onto its side, had completely sunk into soft mud at the bottom of the river. The wreck stubbornly refused to give up its secret treasure. After fifty years or so, the French could not contain their curiosity any longer and decided on a once-and-for-all, no-expense-spared, salvage operation. If the treasure was there, they were going to get it. It was a huge engineering challenge.

A unique and ingenious plan to lift the wreck clear of her muddy grave was conceived. An enormous, piled structure was constructed around the wreck and a sturdy work-platform built on the top, well above the water level. A large number of steel spears with screwed ends were driven down through the mud and into the well-preserved hull, along its entire length. Chains attached to the ends of the spears were then, one by one, winched up a few inches at a time. Over a period of months, the *Telemaque* slowly but surely rose from her grave. Eventually the hull was completely clear of the bottom, though still under water, suspended from the platform. The next phase for the French speculators was to explore the wreck. The engineers needed expert and trustworthy divers, so they called in the English diving firm of Deane and Edwards.

It was never going to be a quick job. There was still a large quantity of mud trapped inside the wreck. John had to empty an entire ship of mud, on his own, by hand and as he shovelled his way into the wreck the disturbed mud reduced the visibility to absolute zero. There were broken timbers, rigging and all manner of debris in his way. He had to feel his way around every item in the total darkness to make sure he was not throwing out something of value. Occasionally he realised he was running his hands over the decomposing corpse of a drowned sailor who had been trapped below deck when the ship had gone down.

Their patience was at last rewarded when John came across some promising-looking barrels. He carefully dug them out and placed them one at a time into a basket in case they fell apart on the way to the surface. Each time the surface crew excitedly hauled up the basket they were bursting with curiosity as to what they had found. The heavier the basket, the more optimistic was their anticipation.

The barrels were eagerly prised open and found to contain fifty-year-old palm oil. That was not very encouraging but John was instructed to carry on digging. Deeper into the wreck John discovered some sturdily built wooden cases bound in iron. This was more like what he was looking for. He bound them carefully with rope, once again to prevent them from falling apart and signalled for them to be hauled up. On the surface the speculators feverishly broke open the cases. Inside they found carefully folded items of mud-stained linen with a decidedly unhealthy smell.

John patiently dug all the way through to the ship's keel and eventually had to report that the *Telemaque* had contained no treasure whatsoever. The disappointed investors in the project had lost their gamble.

The saga of the *Telemaque's* treasure had been followed with great interest by the newspapers on both sides of the channel. As usual, *Punch* magazine was amongst the leaders. On the completion of the project they scooped the rest of the papers claiming to have inside knowledge of the diving operation:

"Deane and Edwards have not gone into minutiae; but we have the means of knowing that the result of the salvage recently concluded has been as follows:

A bit of binnacle
Half-a-yard of yard-arm
A quarter of the quarter-deck
A hen-roost and a portion of the hatchway
A shivered timber
A main-brace and a pair of braces
A part of the cat-head and an old mouse-trap"

Meanwhile, back in England, Charles had by now been released from the lunatic asylum and was still living in London. He had given up active diving and pursued the speculative life of an inventor. Unfortunately, none of his inventions after his smoke helmet came to anything. Strictly speaking even his smoke helmet invention had been a failure since none was ever sold.

He had so far managed to live off the earnings from his earlier diving projects and the commission from the cannons his brother John had raised from the *Royal George*. But that income had dried up and his money was fast running out. Charles was not very good at managing his finances. He suffered from depression and had been twice locked up in a lunatic asylum for his own safety. In Charles's mind, life was not treating him fairly. By now he should have been independently wealthy, famous and being showered with accolades for *his* diving helmet invention.

In a desperate attempt to put matters right, he petitioned the Treasury for a grant to recompense him for *his* invention.

He complained bitterly in his letter to the Treasury and claimed to be the "original inventor of the diving apparatus". He made no reference whatsoever to John's initiativc or contribution. Having originally obtained the rights from the Admiralty to recover the full value of the guns from the *Royal George* he had only been given half their value by the Ordnance. The diving apparatus had been used extensively in recovering property from sunken vessels all over the globe. It had enabled scientific men to make surveys "of the greatest utility for national purposes" and been the means of the Government in making surveys in various parts of the world.

Charles pleaded that *his* invention had cost him much time and expense and it had "ruined his circumstances and impaired his constitution". It seems that he must have suffered badly from the bends at some time which probably also accounts for his having given up diving so early in his career. If the Treasury didn't find in his favour he threatened he would petition the House of Commons.

The Treasury took one look at the Charles's letter and swiftly passed it on to the Board of Ordnance and the Admiralty for their comments. They in turn sloped their shoulders and referred it to Pasley. It is his opinion that ultimately had the greatest influence on the outcome. For reasons best known to himself, Pasley replied "I consider Mr Charles Anthony Deane to have more merit, in bringing the art of diving to perfection, than any other individual".

He made no mention of John Deane. This could only have been the final outcome of William Kemp's poisoning of John Deane's reputation fifteen years previously, and the revenge for John's criticism of Pasley in the *Hampshire Independent* over the merits of the open diving helmet, three years previously. Pasley had ably demonstrated that he knew how to harbour a grudge. He discreetly savoured the sweet taste of his revenge on John.

The Treasury took everything into consideration and generously authorised a payment of £400 to be made to Charles. They qualified their decision by stating that this was on account of the original misunderstanding whereby Charles had been erroneously led to believe he would receive the full value of the guns recovered from the *Royal George*. Before they made the payment, they took the precaution of showing Pasley a draft of their covering letter. Unfortunately, Pasley spotted something he didn't like in the wording and intervened before any money could change hands. He realised that the Treasury's qualification could entitle John to a share of the money as his commission for doing most of the actual diving work in recovering the guns.

As far as Pasley was concerned, John should not receive any reward whatsoever and he requested that the Treasury changed the wording so that Charles received all the money, personally.

The Ordnance Board were not particularly bothered and they did not want to lock horns with Pasley over some trivial wording, so they obligingly complied with his request. At Pasley's suggestion, the letter was therefore changed to "as a gratuity granted to him personally in consequence of the ingenuity and utility of his invention, and of the great benefit that has accrued from the application of it to the Public Service generally, and the Ordnance in particular."

Charles's petition was successful and he received £400 from the Treasury in March 1844.

John was both surprised and delighted to hear of the gratuity and went round to Charles's house. When he broached the subject of a share for his contribution to the invention of the diving helmet, Charles flew into an uncontrolled rage. He garbled on about his smoke helmet and how it was his patent. Though he could not understand it, John slowly came to realise that his loyalty to his older brother had been ill-founded. In the end he decided it would be better to leave before Charles became violent. As he left, Charles angrily slammed the door behind him.

John was deeply disenchanted and disappointed with Charles's inexplicable attitude. He could not understand how Charles could be so selfish and irrational. He thought he was being punished for giving his trust and loyalty so easily. He decided that Charles was being grossly unfair so he appealed to the Board of Ordnance. As expected, they simply confirmed their original decision. John followed up with several more letters justifiably claiming to be the co-inventor, but to no avail.

Without Pasley's blessing, John was on a hiding to nothing.

From this point onwards, whatever was left of the shaky relationship between the two brothers was irrevocably dashed to pieces. They never worked together again and they went their separate ways. Charles had burnt his bridges. He was on his own.

At this point Pasley also makes his exit. Another major engineering problem of national importance had arisen. The country was in the throes of a building boom of a nationwide rail network to meet the insatiable demands of the revolutionary steam locomotive. The railways construction programme was in chaos. The country needed someone who could knock heads together and bulldoze the management through.

Who better than Pasley!

Following his promotion to Major-General he landed the job of Inspector-General Railways. He rode away from the *Royal George* in a blaze of glory to confront a new enemy. There was nothing he liked more than a good fight. His main problem was going to be adjusting his strategy to be effective in the oak-panelled boardrooms of the railway companies. This was fraught with danger because he was being drawn into unfamiliar territory where he could not choose the battleground. He was going to be completely surrounded by civilians and the Rules of Engagement were completely different.

To be fair to Pasley, he did do exactly what he was asked to do and he did bring a semblance of order to where there was once chaos. But whilst his military style of leadership got the job done, it ran against the grain of the civilian protocols. He had made no friends or allies. In fact he made some serious enemies as he marched his way uncompromisingly through the country's bureaucrats and politicians. After six years in the job, the railway companies could tolerate his authoritarian style no more and they mutinied. Pasley had to go.

The end came in true civil service style. He was given a knighthood and sent back to the Royal Engineers at Chatham, with thanks.

The storm clouds were also gathering over the Deane brothers and their lives were running into troubled waters.

Charles sent off another of his unworkable patent applications, this time for a novel method of propelling vessels. He must have realised that it was never going to work because he never followed up with the specifications and the application failed. He was isolated, living as a widower in menial accommodation in the east end of London. His young children were not with him. They were either in care or farmed out to relatives.

Later the same year, John's wife Agnes, to whom he had been married for twenty-one years and who had mothered their five children, fell ill and died at the young age of forty-four years. John's allegiance to Gosport was weakening. He had closer friends in Whitstable and he still had young children to look after. So within a year of Agnes's untimely death, John moved himself and his family back to Whitstable in 1845.

Charles was becoming increasingly disillusioned with his life. He was obsessed with the idea he was a great inventor and he would eventually become rich and famous through one of his brilliant ideas. In 1847 he tried once more and applied to the Admiralty with an impractical "*Plan for better fortifying the coast*" and a flawed design for a 90-gun ship. After a few exchanges of correspondence his proposals died a death.

The year 1848 began badly for John. One of his trading vessels, the brig *Industrious*, which he owned with his business partners, was caught in a squall as it entered the river Tay, near Dundee in Scotland and was wrecked. Tragically all the crew were drowned. It also began badly for Charles when Jane, the wife of his son Charles Junior, died.

In June, Tom Steele, an Irish friend and noted politician who had dived with Charles on the wreck of the *Intrinsic* in County Clare and with John on the *Mary Rose*, committed suicide by jumping off Waterloo Bridge in London. He hadn't died quickly. He was hauled from the water by a passing boatman, half drowned, and carried into nearby King's Hospital. He survived the drowning but he had swallowed a quantity of the polluted Thames water. It was said that "If you fell into the Thames, you didn't drown, you decomposed" and that is exactly what happened to poor Tom Steele. He died a horrible lingering death over the next few weeks.

By November, Charles was in a state of deep depression. Despite everything, in his mind the world didn't appreciate him. Worse still, he had no income and his funds had run out. His dreams of becoming a rich inventor had come to nothing. He had alienated all his friends and family. He had married for a second time three years previously but the marriage had not gone well. He and his wife were living unhappily above a small shop at 5 Providence Place, Commercial Road East in Limehouse, in the dirty docklands of London. He had been miserable for several days, not going out or talking to anyone and he was again living in fear of being dragged off to thc lunatic asylum.

At about six o'clock on the morning of Tuesday, 7th November, his wife Mary was awakened by his getting out of bed twice to get some water. A little later he asked her to go and get him some more water. After she had left the bed, Charles sat up, raised a cutthroat razor to his neck and sliced from ear to ear.

Charles closed the razor and fell back, dead.

His blood spurted everywhere. Mary's long nightdress was drenched head to toe. Her piercing screams brought neighbours rushing to her door. Someone summoned a surgeon named Walford who lived nearby. He was not pleased at being disturbed so early in the morning but reluctantly got dressed and walked around to Charles's apartment. He found Charles lying in a pool of blood on his bed, the closed razor by his side. He put on his spectacles and leaned over the body. He parted the incision in Charles's throat, had a good look around, grumbled something and pronounced him to be "quite dead". He noted objectively that Charles had severed his "left carotid artery, jugular vein and all the principal arteries".

Two days later, an inquest was held before the Coroner, Mr W Baker, in the Lord Hood public house in Rich Street, just round the corner. With Charles's blanched body on view in an open coffin before them, the jury returned a verdict on the cause of his death being due to "temporary insanity". This was a sympathetic verdict designed to sidestep the ruling that suicide victims could not be buried in consecrated ground. Sadly his place of burial has never been found.

Charles did at least achieve one of his objectives through his desperate action. The papers across the country ran the story of his death. He would have approved of the headline:

"Suicide of the Inventor of the Diving Apparatus."

Recognition at last!

Part Four
Horrors and Heroism

16
Back to Whitstable

John Deane found sanctuary back in Whitstable when he arrived there in 1845. He was in a whole community of like-minded souls though many of them were now competitive souls. The population of divers in the town was growing steadily. Here he could feel genuinely at home. His professional diving partner William Edwards lived there, as did his other two business partners, Philpot Wood and Dr James Williams.

John had become particularly close to the Browning family who were related to the Bell and Gann families by strategic marriages. Matthew Browning Senior had built up a large and profitable coal merchant business in conjunction with his ownership of several trading brigantines. His two sons, Thomas and Matthew Junior, were accomplished mariners. His daughter Sarah - well, she was pretty in a homely way, intelligent, and good company. In fact the eighteen-year-old Sarah rather looked up to John. He was different from the other men in the town. He was educated and well-mannered yet he could hold his own against any trouble maker. Most troublemakers instinctively steered clear of him. He was an adventurer and a man of the world. In short, he was her hero and she adored him.

The Brownings lived in a large attractive house called Island Cottage on Island Wall, a stone's throw from the sea. Fortunately it is still standing and is just a short walk from Dollar Row, The King's Head and Copeland House. It was a happy family home. John lodged there, and Sarah willingly helped to look after his five children, aged between eight and sixteen, before John moved into a house of his own.

Island Wall consisted of an ancient earthen defence, which had been built up along the shore to protect the low-lying land on the other side from flooding. Even so, the risk of flooding was never completely eliminated. The flood-prone low-lying land behind the Wall is called the Salts, the name having been handed down from Roman times, when the invaders had exploited the periodic flooding of the area to claim salt from the sea.

The newly built Whitstable harbour provided a safe haven for John's latest diving boat, the *Lalla Rookh*, as well as his trading vessels, the brig *Industrious* and a schooner, which by a strange coincidence was called *Royal George*. He and William Edwards leased a storehouse near the Horsebridge for all their equipment and boating stores. They later bought the land and converted it into what today is a pleasant seaside residence known as Stag Cottage.

By this stage, John's professional reputation was acclaimed across the country. He was in demand with Trinity House, Lloyds of London and some of Britain's top civil engineers including Walker and Burges, James Meadows Rendel and Coode and Smith. Some of the prestigious projects in which he was involved included the new Admiralty Pier at Dover Harbour and a new wall alongside the Houses of Parliament in London.

In Whitstable itself, John was something of a celebrity, though he tended to lead a private life.

Over the next few years, he continued with his successful business as a diver and submarine surveyor. He recovered treasure from the wreck of the HEIC *Earl of Abergavenny* which had sunk near Weymouth in 1805. She had been outward bound for India and China with a cargo including bullion valued at over £200,000 when she had struck on the Shambles, a treacherous shallow bank near Portland. The ship finally foundered in sixty feet of water taking with her some 300 men out of the crew of 400.

The tragedy had provided a popular topic for the country's newspapers. Her master, who had gone down with his ship, was Captain John Wordsworth, none other than the brother of William, the famous poet. William was deeply affected by his brother's death and his poetry assumed a more sombre mood for the remainder of his days.

The local interest in John's adventurous career was considerable. The Whitstable Young Men's Mental Improvement Society persuaded him to give a series of lectures in the Assembly Rooms on the subject of "Diving and Submarine Operations". This was no hardship for John as he had previously given a similar series of talks to the Portsmouth and Portsea Literary and Philosophical Society and the Gosport and Alverstoke Literary Society. It was standing room only in the Assembly Rooms as John made his way up to the podium to deliver his lectures. The crowd was hushed as they listened in awe. After giving a brief summary of historical attempts at diving, John described how he and Charles had developed the diving helmet. He carefully explained the physical principles involved and how Charles and he had learnt about them the hard way. He ended the series with an explanation of exploding gunpowder under water using the voltaic battery, a subject in which he was now the foremost authority in the country.

The climax came with the detonation of a fairly large charge of gunpowder just off the beach. John carried the charge two hundred feet out into the sea at high water and buried it in the seabed. He then returned and detonated the charge using his voltaic battery. The large explosion "produced a considerable concussion, report and commotion of the water, and was witnessed by several hundred persons". The windows of the entire township were rattled by the explosion. Not a soul in Whitstable was left in any doubt that the country's underwater explosives expert had moved in.

But the best ever opportunity for John to publicise his accomplishments to the world as a helmet diver and co-inventor of the diving helmet came in 1851. He was now at the peak of his career.

In May 1851, The Great Exhibition of the Works of Industry of all Nations opened in The Crystal Palace in Hyde Park, London. This colossal event was the brainchild of Prince Albert, Queen Victoria's consort. The magnificent glass structure, over 600 yards long, was the brilliant design of Joseph Paxton. By the end of the year, over six million people, many of whom had come from overseas, had passed through its doors to view the 13,000 exhibits.

It was here that John mounted an exhibit showing models of his open diving helmet and dress. The main feature was a sixty-gallon glass tank in which he had working models of divers wearing his equipment. He demonstrated the provision of air to the model divers by operating a diver's air pump alongside. A prominent sign declared this was "The Diving Apparatus, the original invention of Charles and John Deane". Other articles of interest accompanying the exhibit included artefacts he had recovered from the *Mary Rose, Royal George* and the *Enterprise*.

But ominously, the competition was also there in strength. Two different versions of the close diving helmet were on display at exhibits by Augustus Siebe and a new arrival, C E Heinke.

John acknowledged them in his entry in the official Exhibition catalogue. He said "Some very well-made diving dresses are exhibited in the north-west gallery of the exhibition, in which, however, there are numerous complications, without, we think, proportionate advantages. The more free the helmet used in the water is from screws, nuts and other protuberances, the less likely is the diver to become fixed in the tangled rigging".

Nevertheless, the Siebe exhibits walked off with two prize medals and C E Heinke with the First Class Medal. Siebe was now concentrating on the manufacturing of diving equipment and a variety of accessories, such as voltaic batteries and associated exploding equipment. All his traditional products had been relegated to second place. His business was growing rapidly thanks to his early, privileged foothold in the manufacturing of the Deane diving dress.

Charles Edwin Heinke was the son of another Prussian immigrant who had arrived in Britain in 1808. They had established a successful business as coppersmiths in Great Portland Street, London. Heinke had taken an interest in diving equipment around the time that Pasley had been clearing the wreck of the *Royal George* and he had produced his first diving helmet in 1844. By 1851 he had developed his design of diving helmet to such an advanced level that he beat Siebe into second place at the Crystal Palace Exhibition.

The Siebe and Heinke companies became the two main manufacturers of diving equipment in Britain for the next hundred years and competed fiercely against each other. Many more manufacturers jumped on the bandwagon as the demand for diving equipment grew in Britain and abroad. Diving was fast developing into a *bona fide* industry in its own right.

Rather strangely, Charles Deane's name also appeared on the list of exhibitors at the Crystal Palace. This turned out to be the late Charles's son, by the same name. He had built a model steam engine which he had placed on display. Charles Deane Junior had been apprenticed to Augustus Siebe as a young man and grown up to become one of his principal engineers. He eventually became heavily involved in building Siebe's new ice-making machines and when Siebe exported one of them to Melbourne, Australia he took the opportunity to emigrate. Though he had worked as his father's diving attendant many times and even carried out a few dives himself, he never pursued a career as a diver. One observer described him as "of slender figure, and apparently of weak constitution", so he didn't possess the right physique that would lend itself to a diving career in the first place.

John became entrenched in his opinion that his open helmet design was superior to the close helmet now being built by an increasing number of manufacturers. He stubbornly refused to acknowledge publicly the risk of flooding when his open helmet tilted away from the vertical. However, he did privately appreciate that the problem needed to be minimised. He revealed his concerns when he applied for a patent for *An Improved Construction of Diving Helmet* in 1853. In the application he at last conceded that when the diver tilted, "the tendency is to diminish the capacity of the helmet for containing air". So without going so far as to re-invent the loose flange arrangement of the close dress, one of his improvements was to make "an elastic waterproof continuation to the helmet in the form of a tippet or jacket, so as to increase the capacity of the air chamber, and thereby keep the ordinary water level below the shoulders".

To all intents and purposes, John was converting his open helmet into a close helmet, but with an elastic seal between the helmet and dress instead of a bolted one as George Edwards had introduced.

John decided the cost and effort of a full patent was not worthwhile. He never completed his patent application by sending in a complete specification so it was never registered. He was too busy with his marine civil engineering projects in any case. Around this time he was working for Trinity House surveying a beacon on the treacherous Goodwin Sands. He later dived on the Shambles, the notorious shoal off Portland, Dorset which had been responsible for the wreck of the *Earl of Abergavenny* many years previously. His task was to investigate the suitability of the seabed for the construction of a beacon. He reported on his findings at the Institution of Civil Engineers to an audience including James Meadows Rendel (the President), John Scott Russell and Sir John Rennie.

Apart from the regular work that John attracted from the country's eminent civil engineers, he never gave up on trying to obtain contracts from the Admiralty. But they consistently refused all his offers.

Until suddenly, in 1854, everything changed.

17
It's War

Russia had been progressively expanding its empire to the east and south for the past seventy-five years or so.

Just above the north-east corner of the Mediterranean Sea, the Russians had driven the Turks out of the Crimea and yet further south. But they still had a long way to go before they reached their major strategic objective, the Mediterranean Sea itself.

They had a powerful fleet in the Black Sea, based at Sebastopol in the Crimea. But the fleet was effectively locked up in to the Black Sea because the passage into the Mediterranean was controlled by Turkey, entrenched on both sides of the narrow Bosphorus Straits. On the western bank stood Constantinople (now Istanbul) and on the eastern bank, Scutari. Turkey enforced a strict policy that no ship of war could pass through the Straits without their permission.

In order for Russia to be able to move freely in and out of the Mediterranean, it first had to conquer Turkey and thus neutralise Turkey's command of the Bosphorus Straits.

Hostilities between Russia and Turkey had raged through 1853 as Russian forces pushed south. It reached a climax in November when a Russian fleet inflicted a punishing defeat on the Turks at Sinope in the Black Sea. To the horror of the rest of Europe, it looked as though Turkey could soon fall to the Russians, with undesirable military and commercial consequences. The direct and prompt result was the unlikely alliance between Britain and France on the side of Turkey.

War was declared on Russia in March 1854.

The conflict involved two main arenas, the Baltic Sea and the Black Sea, with the latter being the more crucial. In the Crimea, the strategic target of the Allies was the fortified city of Sebastopol with its extensive natural harbour and a massive dry dock complex. It was the home of the powerful Russian Black Sea Fleet.

Britain and France sent the best of their combined armies and navies to the Crimea with but one, simple objective - to take Sebastopol. It was confidently expected that such a massively superior force would quickly overwhelm the Russians.

The two armies were landed at Eupatoria, sixty miles north of Sebastopol. As soon as they got themselves organised, they marched south, engaging the Russians in a succession of bloody battles including

Alma, Balaclava and Inkerman. The Battle of Balaclava was where the gallant though tragic Charge of the Light Brigade was enacted. The Russians were forced back on each occasion, finally retreating to within the walls of Sebastopol in complete disarray. They fully expected the Allies to follow them inside and to suffer a humiliating defeat within hours. But when the Allies reached the gates of Sebastopol, they were uncertain as to how well it would be defended. They also mistakenly thought it might even have been a trap, and so they hesitated.

The Russians could not believe their good luck.

They immediately took full advantage of the prevarication of the allied forces. They regrouped and set about rebuilding the damaged defences. By the time the Allies made their minds up to attack, it was too late. Sebastopol proved to be too strong a fortress and the besieged Russians too resilient. The fleeting opportunity for a swift victory had been lost.

So began the epic and protracted siege of Sebastopol.

The Russians had previously seen that there was a possibility they might eventually have to retreat into Sebastopol following the Battle of Alma, so as part of the contingency plan for its defence, they had brought in a major proportion of their Black Sea fleet of warships and merchantmen into the protection of the harbour and had sunk a line of their oldest battleships as block ships across its entrance. These included two 120-gun ships, two 88-gun frigates and two corvettes. To make absolutely sure the Allies could not force their way into the harbour they later scuttled a second row of block ships, inside the first. It was a natural harbour, about four miles long and half a mile wide.

Eventually, having retreated within the walls of Sebastopol itself, the Russians scuttled all their remaining ships that had been taking shelter inside the harbour. A total of one hundred and six vessels in all were sunk. The purpose of the desperate measure was to prevent their ships from falling into the hands of the Allies, but with the hope that they could be raised again after the war was over.

Lord Raglan, who was in overall command of the British military operations in the Crimea, was under the mistaken impression that Sebastopol would quickly fall to the Allies. So he ordered arrangements to be made to clear a way through the block ships as soon as the Russian forces had been defeated and driven away. To make sure it would be achieved with certainty, he instructed both the Army and the Navy to prepare separate plans.

First off the mark was the Army.

Back in Britain, the Army's Board of Ordnance, with admirable speed of response, assembled a party of four Royal Sappers and Miners and two civilian divers named John Orchard and John Gordon to be sent to the Crimea. Both civilian divers had originally come from Guernsey in the Channel Islands. John Gordon had been involved in the building of the Alderney Breakwater but was working in the Crystal Cistern at the Panopticon in London's Leicester Square demonstrating the diving helmet and dress to the public when he received the request. The urgency was such that he only had a few hours' notice to pack his bags and get to his waiting ship.

Why didn't they ask John Deane to help? He was the obvious choice. Why did they choose two obscure divers with no great credentials or capabilities for the job? The answer was that the Royal Sappers and Miners were involved, so that Pasley, now Lieutenant-General of the Royal Engineers, was once more back in the picture. Any suggestion of John being called in to help would have got no further than his desk. Gordon and Orchard were of course cheaper to hire than John and that appealed to Pasley, regardless of their lesser skills.

The Army party was equipped with a large quantity of explosives complete with four voltaic batteries, eight miles of electrical wires and four complete sets of helmet diving equipment. The ship waiting to transport them to the Crimea on her maiden voyage was the magnificent screw steamship *Prince*. She was already loaded with the 46th Regiment plus munitions, medical supplies and the main supply of winter clothing for the troops in the Crimea valued at £500,000.

As the *Prince* made her way through the Bosphorus Straits, she made a scheduled stop at Constantinople where she was intended to offload the medical supplies for the hospital at Scutari. But the medical supplies had been the first items of cargo to be loaded, so they were underneath all the munitions and other heavy items. There was no time to unload and then reload the entire ship just to get the medical supplies ashore, so she sailed on to the Crimea. It was a fiasco. The loading of the ship had been completely mismanaged.

The *Prince* duly arrived at Balaclava in the Crimea on 7th November 1854. It was bitterly cold and windy. The troops were shivering in their trenches waiting for their winter clothes. The wind was so strong and blustery that it wasn't safe for the ship to attempt to enter the narrow inlet at Balaclava. So the captain decided to anchor outside and wait for calmer weather. The following day a small steamer shuttled the troops ashore, many of them by now suffering badly from seasickness as well as the cold. Several other transport ships lay at anchor outside the harbour in the atrocious conditions also awaiting their turn to offload cargo. The divers and their kit on the *Prince* were not so lucky and they were ordered to wait onboard until the weather improved and the ship could dock in the harbour.

Unfortunately the weather deteriorated even further and on the morning of 14th November it turned into a regular storm.

The ships inside the harbour fared reasonably well, but those outside were exposed to the full ferocity of a hurricane and the heavy seas. Some of the ships were able to get up steam and escape from the luring rocky shore. Others put their trust in their anchors. That fateful night, in just two hours, thirty-four of the ships outside Balaclava either foundered or were driven onto the rocks and dashed to pieces. Amongst these was the *Prince*. Only one midshipman and seven men survived the wreck. They had managed to clamber onto the rocks and were hauled up the side of a 250-foot cliff by crews from Balaclava. By the loss of this single ship, the British troops in the Crimea were robbed not only of their winter clothing and precious medical supplies, but also of the Army's diving team and their special explosive equipment. Onshore, all the army's tents were blown down during the night and the troops spent the next day in wind and freezing rain without any food, shelter or proper clothing. Many men and horses died of exposure.

If it had not been for Pasley's penny-pinching and prejudiced opinion of John Deane, it could have been John who was lost on the *Prince*. Pasley had unwittingly saved John's life.

The Navy, on the other hand, adopted a more considered approach to planning the clearance of the block-ships.

They decided, first of all, that the explosive charges needed to do the job properly would have to be very large indeed. So large in fact, that they would have to be designed specially for the task. The Admiralty therefore enlisted two of the greatest engineers in Britain with the experience required to undertake the commission. These were the civil engineer James Meadows Rendel and the armaments manufacturer, William Armstrong of Newcastle.

Between the two of them, they came up with the ultimate destructive mine, or "blasting cylinder". It was over twelve feet long, four feet in diameter and weighed five tons. An internal cylinder held one ton of gunpowder and this was surrounded by an air-filled chamber. The theory was that the surrounding air would momentarily protect the exploding gunpowder from the water, which might otherwise prevent all the powder from igniting. The air chamber also provided a large amount of buoyancy and greatly reduced the weight of the cylinder once it was submerged, so making it easier for the diver to manhandle it into position.

To make sure they had enough to finish the job, the Admiralty placed an order for twelve blasting cylinders, and twelve more smaller ones at half a ton each for good measure. They planned to detonate five of the large cylinders simultaneously against the block ships using voltaic batteries. With such a large explosion they hoped that the foundations of the two adjacent Russian forts protecting the entrance to the harbour, Forts Constantine and Alexander, would also be severely affected and rendered untenable. The Admiralty then sought out the most capable man in the country to carry out the critical underwater project.

That was John Deane of Whitstable.

Fortunately, the Admiralty did not have to consult Lieutenant-General Pasley otherwise the story may have had a different ending. Furthermore, the eminent civil engineer James Rendel personally insisted that John was placed in charge of the blasting cylinders because he had worked with him on many occasions in the past. Rendel knew that John was by far the best man in the country for the job.

But when they tried to find John they discovered he was in Dunkirk, France, busily working on a wreck.

Urgent messages were sent out that he was to report to the Admiralty as soon as possible. When he arrived back in Whitstable harbour from France aboard the schooner *Armin* on 5th October, he was immediately appraised of the Admiralty's directive.

After all those years of beating a path to the Admiralty's door to plead for work, it was the Admiralty who ultimately came knocking on his door to ask him for his services.

The irony was not lost on John.

For him, this was the greatest moment in his long and distinguished career. It was a chance at last to show the Military his true capabilities. And to top it all, it was an opportunity to make a significant and personal contribution to the country's war effort. He had dreamt of having adventurous battles on the high seas during his youthful voyages with Fighting Tom Larkins during the Napoleonic War. Now, at last, he had a chance to live that dream, though paradoxically this time the French were his ally and the enemy was Russia.

The Admiralty contract was like an answer to a prayer. They requested him to take three assistant divers. John therefore employed his diving partner William Edwards and two young promising Whitstable divers named James Rigden and George Allen. A Royal Engineers officer by the name of Captain de Moylens and two Sapper divers were assigned to his party to assist with his operations. A written agreement was hurriedly drawn up and signed by Sir Baldwin Walker on 18th October 1854 on behalf of the Admiralty to formalise the arrangements. John's team was given the official title of "The Admiralty Diving Staff in the Crimea".

John was to be responsible directly to Admiral Sir Edmund Lyons, Commander-in-Chief of the Royal Navy in the Crimea.

John's baggage of nearly one hundred tons of explosive cylinders were loaded aboard the brand new iron screw steamer *Robert Lowe* at Woolwich, together with four million Minnie Rifle cartridges for the Army and medical supplies. The ship then sailed round to Portsmouth where John and his diving team embarked along with over five hundred officers and men.

John left his children in the good care of Sarah Browning in Whitstable. She was now a young woman of twenty-seven years of age. She was still single and enjoyed looking after his children. Sarah also looked after John's business affairs during his absence, acting as his agent whilst he was away. His diving operations should take only a few weeks at the most and he would soon be back home.

The *Robert Lowe*'s voyage to Balaclava did not go smoothly. The competence of the ship's captain and the crew was called into question. When the ship docked at Malta, Rear Admiral Stewart reported that there was disorder and insubordination amongst the officers due to their "intemperate habits". However, John's assignment was too crucial to delay the ship's voyage just to discipline the offending officers in Malta, so it was ordered to sea once more. There was just one more short stop at Constantinople where the medical supplies for Scutari were due to be offloaded. Unbelievably, they had made the same mistake as they had made with the *Prince*. The medical supplies were underneath John's blasting cylinders and the munitions and they could not be unloaded and once again the hospital had to watch their medical supplies sail on to the Crimea. The *Robert Lowe* eventually reached Balaclava on 4th January.

Back in London, an official inquiry was held by the Admiralty into the behaviour of the captain and his officers, which ended in the abrupt termination of the captain's contract. The issue had been exacerbated by the inappropriate loading of the ship's cargo at Woolwich.

The siege of Sebastopol should have been over by the time the *Robert Lowe* arrived but there was no sign of the Russians giving in. Since the Russians were able to maintain heavy fire on any ships attempting to breach the block-ships, the use of the blasting cylinders was delayed indefinitely. So for convenience they were left on board the *Robert Lowe* and the medical supplies remained inaccessible. The issue grew into a major embarrassment.

In the meantime, the *Robert Lowe* undertook the duty of transferring up to 900 sick and wounded soldiers at a time across the Black Sea to the hospital at Scutari where Florence Nightingale was going about her revolutionary nursing duty. On one such voyage, in May, the ship brought Miss Nightingale over from Scutari to Balaclava. She brought with her a retinue of attendants including cooks and a drummer boy, so there was little doubt about her personal authority. The 'Lady of the Lamp' was not at all pleased with the under-engined ship either. An eighty-six horse power steam engine was making heavy weather of pushing 1296 tons of ship through the water. So she nick-named it the

"*Robert Slow*".

During her trip across the Black Sea she discovered the debacle over the medical stores trapped under John's blasting cylinders. Miss Nightingale immediately joined the chorus of voices calling for the unloading of the one hundred tons of blasting cylinders to get at the medical supplies. With the personal backing of Lord Panmure, the Minister for War, Miss Nightingale wielded considerable influence. She appealed directly to Lord Raglan who, following a meeting with John, then issued the necessary orders to get the cylinders and medical supplies unloaded. So thanks to Miss Nightingale, John now had his entire stock of explosives and detonating apparatus safely ashore and at his immediate disposal.

Lord Raglan was painfully aware that John's original objective in the Crimea was no longer feasible, at least for the time being. But now that John and his team of divers were at his disposal, he was not going to let such a valuable asset get away from him. There were many underwater tasks that needed doing. The most pressing of these was to support the imminent attack on the towns of Kertch and Yenikale. These were two fortified towns protecting the entrance to the Sea of Azoff at the eastern corner of the Crimea.

But the Russians had anticipated a possible allied expedition into the Sea of Azoff and were preparing a secret weapon in the Kertch Straits to sink an invading fleet. They had developed two types of marine mines. One was a moored contact mine that floated just below the surface and exploded when a ship bumped into it. The other type was laid on the seabed and was detonated remotely by an operator using voltaic batteries, when he could see that an enemy ship was in a position above the mine.

Some Royal Navy ships had already been badly damaged by these "infernal machines" in the Baltic campaign so they were aware that the Russians had a new secret weapon. Lord Raglan was therefore justifiably concerned that the Russians may have laid a trap for his ships if they tried to enter the Sea of Azoff. As a further obstacle, the Russians had scuttled a row of block-ships across the entrance to the Sea.

Nevertheless, a combined British and French fleet was sent off. Troops were landed south of Kertch and they marched immediately on the two towns. The Russians were taken by surprise and they put up very little resistance. Following a short battle, Kertch and Yenikale fell into Allied hands.

The timing of the Allied attack turned out to have been extremely fortuitous. The Russians had been in the process of laying out their minefield in the Straits of Kertch and had been preparing to commission the deadly mines when the attack had taken place. The mines were intended to be exploded remotely by electrical detonation from voltaic batteries on board a 150-ton hulk moored offshore. Fortunately, they had not quite finished their work and the invading ships had sailed unharmed through the minefield.

John and his divers carefully disconnected the wires and gathered in the unexploded mines. They also discovered a large number of the contact-type infernal machines stored in the hold of the hulk, which had been awaiting deployment. Had the attack taken place a few weeks later, there might have been a very different outcome.

The hazardous work they carried out in clearing the mines at the entrance to the Sea of Azoff represents the first ever use of divers for this duty. This type of work now forms a major part of the duties carried out by the Royal Navy's divers today. After making the area safe by the clearance of the Russian infernal machines, John and his team set about blasting a passageway through the block-ships and opened up the entrance to the Sea of Azoff to the Allies. The attack on Kertch and Yenikale represented a very important strategic victory.

Captain Lyons RN, the son of Admiral Lyons in charge of the British naval forces in the Crimea, then grasped the initiative and led a small group of shallow-draft steam vessels in a daring expedition into the Sea of Azoff.

What happened next is regarded as one of the most important operations the Royal Navy undertook during the entire war.

And John Deane was to play a pivotal role.

18
First blood

The British public were becoming increasingly disenchanted with the war in the east.

The promised fall of Sebastopol was not being delivered. The tragic loss of life through disease and injuries was making distressing news back home. The Royal Navy in particular came under heavy fire from the public for their apparent lack of success. It was the acid wit of *Punch* magazine that inflicted one of the most painful wounds with the cutting words:

"The fleet in the Baltic was expected to do everything, and did nothing.
The fleet in the Black Sea was expected to do nothing, and did it."

This criticism was perhaps a little harsh and it certainly did not reflect the truth about Captain Edmund Moubray Lyons's naval expedition into the Sea of Azoff in 1855. Captain Lyons led the way in his steamship *Miranda*. He headed directly north across the Sea of Azoff to the town of Berdiansk. He bombarded the town and sent raiding parties ashore, destroying several ships and a large quantity of stored grain. He moved on to Genitchesk where he encountered a strong force of Russian infantry heavily armed with field guns. Despite the formidable opposition, seventy-three Russian ships were set ablaze together with large stores of grain on shore, with the loss of none of his own men.

After only four days, the audacious captain was able to report to his father that no less than 250 Russian ships had been burnt and sunk, most of them laden with vital supplies for the Russian army. Before rejoining the fleet at Kertch, Captain Lyons attacked the strongest of the Russian fortresses at Taganrog, destroying government buildings and further stores, followed by attacks on Mariopol and Gheisk.

The naval expedition was an astonishing tactical success.

John Deane followed closely in the wake of Captain Lyons's adventures in the Sea of Azoff. He was tasked with surveying the wrecks for possible salvage and any re-usable materials such as anchors, chain cables, boilers, funnels and paddle wheels. He was also required to make sure that any scuttled Russian warships were damaged beyond repair so they could not be recommissioned.

Leaving the rest of his team at Kertch, John set off in HM Steamer *Vesuvius* and sailed across the Sea of Azoff to meet up with

Captain Sherard Osborne on the steam transport HMS *Manilla*. Captain Osborne, who was attacking the town of Genitchi at the time, was in charge of the British squadron in the Sea of Azoff. He issued an order for John to proceed onwards to Berdiansk on HM Steamer *Ardent* with the gunboat HMS *Boxer* in tow.

When they steamed into the bay at Berdiansk they were able to witness the destruction that Captain Lyons had recently wreaked on the Russian ships at anchor there. In the bay, seventy vessels lay burnt, including four men-of-war steamers scuttled in shallow water by the Russians. One of these was the jewel in the crown of the Russian Black Sea Fleet, the *Maloditz,* bearing the flag of Rear-Admiral Wolff.

Ardent and *Boxer* anchored near the scuttled Russian steamers. Everything was quiet and there was no sign of life on the shore close by. *Ardent* lowered one of her boats with John and his party aboard and they rowed over to the wrecks. John inspected the steamers closely, methodically developing his plan to destroy them with explosives.

As he was standing on top of the boiler of one of the Russian war steamers inspecting the machinery, he suddenly found himself in the midst of a hail of bullets. A group of mounted Cossacks had opened fire on him from behind a building on the shore. He quickly retreated behind the machinery and climbed into *Ardent's* boat. The crew returned rifle fire as they hurriedly rowed their way back to the gunboat. Fortunately, nobody was hit.

The *Boxer* in the meantime had heard the shots and was preparing her guns to fire back at the Cossacks. Their "noble 68 pounder" sent a shot whistling over John's head and into the building followed by a shrapnel shell from one of their 24-pounder howitzers. This had the desired effect and a number of Cossacks were spotted galloping away along the cliff.

The *Ardent* returned to Kertch where John made preparations for a return visit to Berdiansk, this time with the specific objective of destroying the four scuttled men-of-war steamers. He loaded up the schooner *Glance* with a number of his smaller blasting cylinders and detonating equipment and sailed north once more.

This time Captain Sherard Osborne sent the gunboat HMS *Beagle*, commanded by Lieutenant William Hewett, to Berdiansk to rendezvous with the *Glance* and offer some protection. Lieutenant Hewett had already won a reputation for bravery just a few months previously. He had been in charge of a Lancaster Gun in a shore battery outside the walls of Sebastopol. A band of Russian soldiers attacked the battery from the rear and got within three hundred yards. Hewett received orders to spike the gun and retreat, but he refused to desert his gun, making the excuse that he had not received the order from his Commanding Officer.

Together with his crew of seamen and some soldiers, Hewett turned the gun round, shot away the rear of the parapet of his battery and opened fire on the advancing Russian party. The Russians changed their minds and retreated. The exploit won Hewett promotion and the Victoria Cross. He eventually died in 1888 with the rank of Vice-Admiral.

Under the protection of Hewett on the *Beagle*, John sailed the *Glance* over and tied up to one of the scuttled Russian war ships. He set to work warily preparing his explosive charges. After a short while the bullets suddenly started to rain down on him again. This time the *Beagle* was ready and immediately returned fire. The Cossacks retreated once more and chose not to interfere with John's operations again. John successfully destroyed all four ships and before returning to Kertch he found and destroyed three more steam warships.

John could not resist the temptation to take a souvenir from the scene of one of his most notable achievements. He decapitated the figurehead of Admiral Wolff's flagship, the *Maloditz*, and when he eventually returned to Sebastopol he presented the severed head to Admiral Sir Edmund Lyons. This beautiful gilded trophy is now on display in Arundel Castle, Sussex, which was the Admiral's home. The trophy was a very poignant one for the Admiral. The credit for the sinking of the Russian flagship went justifiably to his son, Captain Lyons who had conducted the very successful naval expedition into the Sea of Azoff. But the Captain was shot in the leg a little later, during a land assault on Sebastopol and he died shortly afterwards from his wound. The trophy therefore represented a fitting memorial to the Admiral's brave son.

Sir Edmund wrote to the Admiralty from his headquarters on HMS *Royal Albert* off Sebastopol to report on John Deane's good work:

"Mr Deane, the submarine surveyor and engineer, who was placed at my disposal by their Lordships, and who it will be seen, has been exceedingly active and useful in destroying, by means of submarine explosions, seven of the steam-vessels which formed the Russian flotilla ..." The Admiralty Diving Staff in the Crimea were covering themselves in glory.

Captain A E Wilmot, Senior Officer on board HMS *Sphinx,* issued the next set of instructions to:

"Mr Deane in command of the Admiralty Diving Staff, Straits of Kertch.

"Continue your valuable operations in raising vessels, destroying wrecks etc. Your zeal and activity in the duties you have undertaken cannot be too highly appreciated and deserve the highest praise with the best of thanks of our Country."

John and his team were rightly pleased and proud of their accomplishments over the past six months, but they were just about to suffer a casualty. Although they were fully prepared for the dangers associated with their submarine activities and the gunfire of the Russian Cossacks, there were far more lethal dangers spreading through the ranks. These were dysentery and cholera.

The diseases took far more soldiers' lives than the Russian gunfire. For that reason, the Crimean War has been called the greatest military disaster in modern British history. Nobody was safe and survival seemed to be a lottery. Even Lord Raglan himself fell as one of the cholera victims. In John's team, it was William Edwards who drew the short straw. Probably weakened by exposure and fatigue, he fell ill with dysentery in August 1855 and was taken aboard a hospital transport ship lying in Kertch Bay. His conditioned worsened and he contracted cholera. He died on 31st August aboard the ship.

John took the death of William Edwards very hard. He did all he could and arranged for him to be buried ashore at Fort St Paul at Kertch. He had lost a life-long friend and diving partner.

Ten days later, the siege of Sebastopol was over. After innumerable and costly attempts by both the British and French forces, the French initially broke through the fortress's defences and they were quickly followed by the British troops.

The Russians had managed to build and maintain a floating bridge a half a mile long across the harbour throughout the siege and it had provided an invaluable lifeline for the besieged city. The bridge stretched from Fort Nicholas within the walls of Sebastopol across to Fort Michel on the northern shore. As soon as the city's defences were breached, there was a panicked exodus of its entire population across the bridge to safety on the northern side. All that the Allies found in the city amongst the many dead were hundreds of sick and wounded Russian soldiers, the ones who were too sick to escape across the floating bridge.

The battle for Sebastopol may have been over, but not the war. John's contract, which he initially expected to be over in a few weeks, was turning into many months.

19
SEBASTOPOL

Having secured Sebastopol, Lord Panmure, the Minister for War, ordered the city's military assets to be destroyed.

These included an enormous complex of dry docks, which had been originally built by British engineers. The docks provided the essential maintenance and repair facilities for the Russian warships operating in the Black Sea. Without them, the Russians could not maintain an effective fleet and their military power in the region would be significantly reduced. But it would take massive explosions to destroy the granite foundations and dock walls.

Eyes fell on John Deane and what remained of his stockpile of blasting cylinders. John was already riding a wave of popularity with the Navy and the Army, but with this new objective, he was suddenly even more sought after. Lieutenant-Colonel Edward Lloyd, the Commanding Officer of the Royal Engineers in the Crimea, personally requested John's services from Admiral Sir Edmund Lyons. John had finally been accepted by the Royal Engineers. Undoubtedly this would not have happened had Pasley not been sixteen hundred miles away and out of the equation.

The task of destroying the docks was a massive one. A line of three locks led into a large central basin. Five dry docks led off from the basin, three to the south and two to the north which straddled the three entrance locks. The whole complex sat in a natural, rocky valley, so the Allies agreed amongst each other that the job should be shared equally by the British and French forces. The French were allocated the responsibility for destroying the northern half and the British the southern half, consisting of the three dry docks and the basin.

In the choice of deciding whose forces were to destroy which half of the docks, the French had come out the more fortunate. Their docks were completely dry. This meant that they could bury their destructive charges in dry holes dug into the foundations. Unfortunately for the British, much of the southern part of the docks was under a few feet of water, which was being fed by a natural stream coming down from the surrounding hills. This meant that some of the British charges had to be laid under water.

Once again, John's services were proving indispensable.

The Royal Engineers were put in overall charge of the destruction of the docks. They approached the whole project with careful preparations and professional engineering skill. It was essential, that in order to achieve the maximum effect with the least danger to the surrounding troops, the explosions had to take place deep underground. So special shafts and galleries were dug into the walls and foundations. The Engineers brought in 156 Sappers and 300 line soldiers to undertake the exhausting excavation work.

The most effective and reliable method the British had of detonating the huge charges was by means of John's voltaic batteries. This was especially useful for those charges that had to be installed under water. By contrast, in the dry French half of the docks, they were able to detonate their charges by simple trails of gunpowder and fuses.

When each set of excavations in the British half was completed, the charges were installed. John connected up his electrical wires to the underground explosives and ran them back up above ground and away a safe distance. The Engineers built John a special bombproof hut at the head of the docks in which he placed his voltaic batteries and where he could take shelter when he detonated the charges. He had ten batteries in all. The wires led all the way back from the charges into the hut, which needed to be strong enough to protect John from tons of falling masonry. When all was ready, all personnel had been removed a safe distance and John was satisfied with the preparation of his equipment, he closed the circuit with his batteries.

The explosions were the biggest most of the men had ever witnessed in their entire lives. John was getting through several tons of gunpowder each day. Each time, the ground shook as if in an earthquake. Hundreds of tons of granite masonry were hurled into the air. The destructive effect was awesome. The once-magnificent docks were systematically reduced to piles of rubble. The huge steel gates at the entrance to the docks had originally been built for the Russians by Rennie in Britain. They were very valuable and importantly, they were portable. So the gates were floated off and towed all the way back to Britain.

A Russian brig of war had been laid up in one of the dry docks when Sebastopol had fallen to the Allies. John therefore added the destruction of this ship to his list of explosive exploits.

The Times reporter at Sebastopol, William Howard Russell,

who gained fame for being the first ever war correspondent, reported extensively on John's progress on the destruction of Sebastopol Docks. Russell was undoubtedly grateful for the provision of some newsworthy material since there were no more battles to report on. He dubbed John "the infernal diver" in an allusion to his habit of making loud explosions. Russell himself was a controversial character. A soldier described him as a "vulgar low Irishman, sings a good song and drinks anyone's brandy". Nevertheless, Florence Nightingale owed her fame to the coverage which Russell gave her in the pages of *The Times*.

The Russians looked on helplessly at the systematic destruction of their magnificent docks from across the other side of the harbour. They fired their guns from the north side but the range was so great that their shot fell with little accuracy or effect. However, despite the range, the Russians did manage to injure two of the men working on the docks, one soldier losing his arm.

Apart from the risk of being shot, John's efforts proved physically exhausting for him. He was, after all, fifty-five years of age. He had had a tough life and his body was starting to show signs of wear and tear. But fortunately, he had been blessed with a strong constitution and he managed to make it through. His two surviving assistants, James Rigden and George Allen had become very lazy and not as helpful as they should have been. They persistently came up with lame excuses for not diving. John complained in one of his letters to Sarah back at Whitstable:

"A more idle man [Rigden] I think I never had to do with and he is the means of preventing George Allen from being more industrious ... They have nothing whatever to do but to smoke, sleep, eat good food and drink where and as much as they like."

John on the other hand was unstoppable. But his detonations did not all fire as planned. He was using electrical cables that had been used repeatedly throughout the campaign and they were suffering from extensive damage and repairs. But by painstaking checks and further repairs, he was always able to achieve the results he wanted in the end.

On the completion of the destruction of Sebastopol Docks, Lieutenant-Colonel Edward Lloyd RE wrote to His Excellency General Sir William Codrington KCB that he was "indebted to Mr Deane, Submarine Engineer" for his "valuable services in preparing and firing most of the mines by voltaic action" and thanked Admiral Sir Edmund Lyons for having placed John at his disposal. Sir William Codrington was by then the General Commanding the British Forces in the Crimea, having taken over following the death of Lord Raglan from cholera.

John continued with his explosions around Sebastopol on behalf of the Royal Engineers. Anything that had a military application was targeted. His next objective was a group of large buildings used by the Russians as barracks and known as the White Buildings. With the destruction of Sebastopol's military facilities, its strategically important dry docks, and the entire Russian Black Sea fleet, in all of which John had had a hand, the principal objectives of the war with Russia had been achieved. Russia's advance into Turkish territory had been halted and there was no longer any justification to continue with the hostilities. So in March 1856 the opposing sides decided on an armistice.

The war was over.

The adversaries ceased firing at each other and were able to relax. They even approached within twenty feet of each other and conversed as best they could. A healthy trade in exchanging mementoes was quickly established. On one occasion John joined the soldiers along the bank of a river called the Tchernia where they were able to trade with the Russians on the other side. Handkerchiefs, coins and purses were popular commodities criss-crossing the river through mid-air. John exchanged his purse with that of a Russian Officer.

Boredom became a problem amongst the troops whilst they awaited their return to Britain. Brave attempts at entertainment were made. Plays were performed in a large building in the city, the soldiers making a serious attempt at acting. One of the most popular events proved to be a horse race held on Easter Monday and given the grand title, the Sebastopol Spring Meeting. About one hundred of the finest horses in the country were entered and the winner rode off with the surprisingly large prize of £200.

When John was not blowing things up he occasionally dived around Sebastopol harbour to search for anything of value that might have been dumped in the water by the fleeing Russians. He struck lucky when he dived near the ruins of Fort St Paul, close to where the southern end of the floating bridge had been attached. He came upon a battery of field artillery. There were guns and their attached carriages galore together with the decaying remains of the horses that had been forced to haul them into the harbour. As he slowly groped his way through the tangle of artillery pieces he was suddenly confronted by the grinning skeleton of a soldier, held together by the remnants of his uniform and still astride the skeletal remains of his horse, with his foot trapped in its stirrup. This sad spectacle was the result of a desperate action by the retreating Russians to prevent the valuable artillery pieces falling into the hands of the invading Allies.

From this seabed graveyard John extracted twelve brass field pieces including two howitzers and forty carriages. The wood of the carriages had already been badly eaten away by teredo worms in the few months since the fall of Sebastopol but the guns were of considerable value and capable of being brought back into service.

Sir William Codrington was delighted with John's diving work. He wrote:

"I request you will inform me of anything which may be necessary for the prosecution of this public service in order that I may afford you every assistance in my power. It will be my duty hereafter to bring to the notice of the Government and the Admiralty the Service thus rendered by you."

He was a man of his word and made a special point of mentioning John's successful salvage operation in his next dispatch to Lord Panmure in London in April 1856.

John also carried out a large number of less spectacular diving tasks during his Crimean campaign. These included surveying and repairing ships' bottoms after they had collided with the block-ships during the attack on Kertch. He had fitted new steam valves to replace damaged ones and raised a troop-landing vessel, which had sunk during the landings. He recovered a 68-pounder gun and six and half tons of copper. When Admiral Lord Lyons's headquarters ship HMS *Royal Albert* had finally slipped her moorings on her departure, John was able to recover them, leaving nothing that would be useful for the Russians.

In between the tasks he undertook for his military masters, John was able to conduct a certain amount of private business. One of his projects involved his purchase of a wreck that had sunk in fifty feet of water. It carried a cargo of casks full of provisions and he was paid nine pounds for each one he recovered. He had also bought a longboat that had belonged to a merchant ship and had used it for his diving operations at Kertch and in the Sea of Azoff. Together with a small Russian boat he had raised in Sebastopol Harbour, he brought both back to Britain.

John managed to amass a large quantity of trophies and scrap metal. The relics included gun carriage wheels, shot and shell. There was so much that he had to arrange their return to Britain in a separate vessel, the *Triumph*, together with a few of his unused blasting cylinders. He astutely distributed many of his trophies amongst the military hierarchy once back in Britain.

John's efforts in the Crimea were eventually rewarded by the Admiralty. The secretary to Admiral Lord Lyons wrote to him saying:

"Lord Lyons has this day written officially to the Admiralty ... bearing testimony to your zealous, useful and gallant services and he has expressed a hope that their Lordships will be pleased to grant you the Crimea Medal with the Sebastopol and Azoff Clasps."

John had reached the pinnacle of his remarkable diving career. He was not only going to return to Whitstable a true hero, but he had the immense satisfaction of having demonstrated to the Military the usefulness of his diving helmet in the most effective way possible.

He had at last achieved all his life's ambitions.

20
Home

The Army and Navy gave priority to getting their own men back to Britain first. Being civilians, John and his two Whitstable divers had to wait their turn. The troops had nearly all left by the time they secured their places back on the steam transport *Robert Lowe* in June 1856.

When the ship sailed out of Balaclava harbour, she was fully loaded. John shared the ship with 838 men of the Land Transport Corps, thirty officers, six horses, 200 tons of shot and 160 tons of provisions. She must have been loaded to the gunwales. Happily the *Robert Lowe* had an event-free though perhaps slow voyage back to Britain. She made brief stops at Constantinople, Malta and Plymouth and finally set off once more for Portsmouth where she arrived on 4th August.

John was anxious to get back to Whitstable as soon as possible to see his children who were nearly two years older than when he had last seen them. He was also looking forward to seeing Sarah Browning once more. Her letters to him over the past twenty-one months had been particularly affectionate. Some of her sentences were written in a secret code, a kind of shorthand, which has defied deciphering. It is tempting to speculate that these were personal messages of love. She was certainly looking forward to the return of her hero. Unfortunately John was obliged to kick his heels in Portsmouth for a few days to await the arrival of HMS *Triumph*, which was carrying a large consignment of his scrap metal and main collection of trophies

John finally returned to Island Cottage in Whitstable to an emotional homecoming. His son Edmund, the oldest, aged 27 years and three daughters, Agnes, Caroline and Susannah the youngest at 17 years old, were all there to greet him. Sarah, now 29, was of course overjoyed with his return. Their relationship blossomed and within two months they were married at St Alphege church in Whitstable.

John was now a moderately wealthy man. He had managed his finances efficiently throughout his career. His contract with the Admiralty for his Crimean campaign had been based on day rates for him and his team, on the assumption that the work would only take a few weeks. But it had taken nearly two years. The Admiralty paid John handsomely, and included an agreed gratuity of another £200 for a job well done.

He was able to retire on his return from the Crimea to the company of a doting, attractive, 29-year-old wife.

Whitstable had by now become the centre of British helmet diving. The small town had a near-monopoly on the art. Lloyds of London and the Whitstable diving community were virtually a partnership. The phenomenon of this unique relationship attracted the interest of some of the country's most eminent writers, not least of whom was Charles Dickens.

Dickens visited Whitstable on several occasions and met many of the divers, including John Gann. One report even claimed that Dickens actually stayed at Vine Cottage, near Dollar Row, as a guest of John Gann during one of his visits. It is likely that Dickens himself penned the article entitled *"Another Whitstable Trade"* published in 1860 in his newspaper *All the Year Round*. The writer began:

"If it had not fallen to the lot of Whitstable to be celebrated for its oysters, and its company of 'free dredgers,' it might have claimed a word of notice for producing that rarest of all workmen, the sea-diver.

"The Whitstable divers may be from thirty to fifty in number, strong, stout, healthy, temperate men, who look like able-bodied sailors ... They form themselves, by a kind of Whitstable instinct, into a working brotherhood, under the presidency and guidance of a captain - Mr Green. [Undoubtedly a misspelled Gann.]

"In stormy seasons, when the wreck of some heavily-laden homeward-bound vessel is an every-day occurrence round our fatal coast, the rooms at the King's Head Inn, in Whitstable, the house of call for divers, are very thinly attended, and the men, with their boats and apparatus, are hurried off in all directions to profitable work. Mr Green is then in the hourly receipt of telegrams from Lloyds, or from private owners, requesting him to send four divers to 'Moelfre' and four more 'to the Goodwin Sands' ... and his divers are sometimes sent for from the West Indies, and distant, unknown seas. These men go down in their diving dress, until they are sixty or seventy years of age ... May Whitstable always have the honour of producing such bold and dextrous men as plentyfully as she has hitherto done, and may they have the wisdom to keep what they get!"

The reference to Moelfre, a small town in North Wales, refers to the tragic loss of the steam clipper *Royal Charter* in 1859 when 459 people were drowned. She had been homeward bound from Australia to Liverpool carrying a cargo of gold, which the Ganns had been commissioned to recover by Lloyds.

The King's Head in Whitstable had indeed become the house of call for divers at this time. It belonged to John Gann himself. He had knocked two of the end houses in Dollar Row into one to convert them into the Inn. Retired divers frequently invested their hard-earned savings in a public house. George Bell had taken over the Fisherman's Arms just a little further down the road after he had hung up his diving boots.

Another commentator described his experience of visiting Whitstable when he yielded to his curiosity about the novel diving trade. It seems he didn't exactly take to it like a fish to water, which is probably why he chose to remain anonymous:

"I have been now and again to Whitstable, where, I believe by some remarkable process of Nature, every third male person is born a diver. Anyway, Whitstable is the place where divers mostly grow, and where I caught the temptation to go a-diving myself. I should feel grateful to any obliging Anarchist who would blow up Whitstable tomorrow. I mentioned my desire to one or two old divers who had permitted me to make their acquaintance in consideration of a suitable succession of drinks."

On a more serious level, Robert Stephenson MP, the President of the Institution of Civil Engineers in London, remarked at a meeting chaired by Isambard Kingdom Brunel in 1856:

"Nothing had so much contributed to extend and facilitate marine engineering, as the invention of the diving dress."

This was praise indeed coming from the highest level of the most prestigious engineering institution in the land.

Whitstable enjoyed about fifty years of dominance as the prime source of helmet divers in Britain. But the diving industry ultimately outgrew the small harbour town and spread out in all directions. Liverpool in particular became the country's next major centre.

John Deane moved his family to a large and comfortable house at 90 Hardres Street in Ramsgate where the environment was healthier. There was less disease than in Whitstable where tuberculosis and cholera were taking their toll at the time. Ramsgate was also where he had fond memories of starting his family with his first wife, Agnes, and first setting out on his long and adventurous diving career. He bought several properties around the town and lived comfortably off the rental income for the rest of his days.

John remained faithful to his open helmet design to the end and never adopted the close helmet in any of his operations. The open helmet continued to be used by many of the older Whitstable divers of the "Deane school" until the late 1800s. But by 1900, the close helmet version, incorporating the Edwards bolted flange around the corselet, had been universally adopted. The design was so perfect, safe and simple, that it has hardly changed in the intervening 100 years or so. Though it is now considered obsolete in Britain it is still in common use in many parts of the world including eastern Europe and Scandinavia.

Augustus Siebe had retired in 1868 when his health had begun to fail and he died four years later at his home and manufactory in Denmark Street in 1872 aged eighty-four. He had built a huge business selling diving helmets and all the associated equipment that went with them. The diving side of his business had grown to be by far the most popular product and the company became the largest manufacturer of diving equipment in the world. Siebe had lived an honourable life. He had always been well liked and respected. He never made any false claims about the invention of the diving helmet. But after his death all that changed.

Siebe left his business in equal parts to his wayward son Henry and Irish-born son-in-law William Gorman. The responsibility for all technical matters rested squarely on the shoulders of Gorman. He was an accomplished engineer and had been working for Siebe for many years. Henry had to give up his career as an artist to take on his father's business. He knew nothing about diving and ended up in a loose marketing role, spending much of his time unproductively in France. He didn't get involved in the engineering side at all. But what he did do, was to write about the history of his father's company. Over the years, he propagated a lie and wrote consistently about how his father had invented the diving helmet.

In the absence of any contradictory response from the retired and ageing John Deane, Henry Siebe's fabricated version of events gradually and insidiously crept into the literature. One by one, the encyclopaedias picked up and regurgitated Henry Siebe's twisted version and they have blindly promulgated it ever since.

For this reason, virtually every encyclopaedia in the world, even today, still carries the erroneous account that Augustus Siebe invented the diving helmet. They also date Siebe's 'invention' as having taken place in 1819, which is another of Henry Siebe's falsifications. That is the date when his father first arrived in Britain as a non-English-speaking, Prussian immigrant, skilled in watch-making and silver chasing. Probably the first time Augustus Siebe had ever seen the sea was when he crossed the channel on his way to England, let alone know anything about diving.

Henry Siebe was a little over-enthusiastic with his claims for his father. Perhaps it was his predilection for strong drink that led him to make the false claims. He certainly spent a lot of his time boasting about his father's company in public houses frequented by divers when back in England. Indeed, it is poetic that Henry Siebe died in the Diver's Arms in Herne Bay in 1887.

Henry Siebe's mis-information campaign was nevertheless very successful. His dubious legacy to the diving industry was, to all intents and purposes, the complete elimination of the Deanes' involvement in the invention of the diving helmet from the literature.

It sadly lends credence to the saying "Give a lie a good start, and the truth will never catch up".

Perhaps this book will ensure that Henry Siebe's lie will be an exception to the rule.

In his lifetime, John Deane saw the diving helmet launch a whole new industry. By the time he died, it had been adopted in over thirty countries, which straddled the entire globe. Both the Royal Navy and the Army had established diving schools, which generated hundreds of new divers. Major organisations such as the Liverpool Salvage Association, Trinity House, and the railway companies had developed substantial diving capabilities.

Divers were employed in large numbers at every marine civil engineering construction site around the world. The 1800s saw a huge number of new docks and harbours built around the world to accommodate the expanding fleets of steam-powered ships, both military and civilian. Divers regularly performed extraordinary feats of salvage, raising ships or their valuable cargoes.

Today, the annual turnover of the global diving industry is in excess of $3,000,000,000. It supports an annual expenditure of $80,000,000,000 in the subsea industry. The present international offshore oil and gas industry could not have been achieved without the essential contribution of divers.

This is a legacy of which anyone could be proud.

After retiring, John lived another twenty-six years in Ramsgate, which he enjoyed in the company of a close, religious and musical family that included five grandchildren.

After an extraordinary life, John died in 1884 at the ripe old age of eighty-four. He is buried in a modest grave in Ramsgate cemetery together with close members of his family.

About the author

John Bevan has been involved in diving all his life.

He has worked for the Ministry of Defence as a research scientist in diving physiology, for Comex Diving Ltd, a North Sea diving company as Technical, Training and Safety Manager and has been the managing director of his own underwater consultancy company, Submex Ltd, since 1976. In his consultancy role, he has worked for four European governments and most of the major oil companies operating in the North Sea.

Seeing a demand for technical literature for commercial divers, he wrote and published *The Professional Diver's Handbook*. It has become the international best-seller in its field and is currently in its second edition.

He first came to public notice in 1970 when he and a colleague undertook the world record, saturation, chamber dive to 1500 feet. This was the greatest pressure that any human had ever withstood and they crashed through the "Helium Barrier". It was described by the Americans as a "hyperbaric moon-landing"!

In 1990, John helped form The Historical Diving Society and was elected it's founding chairman, a position he still holds. Daughter societies have since been formed in over 20 countries worldwide.

After gaining a PhD in the history of diving, he wrote *The Infernal Diver*, the definitive reference book on the invention of the diving helmet. This was followed by *Another Whitstable Trade*, the definitive history of the global diving industry (in press).

John continues to work as a consultant and has become the UK's leading diving expert investigating diving accidents in litigation cases. He often appears on television as an expert providing commentaries on technical aspects of diving. He is the editor of the diving trade magazine *Underwater Contractor International* and the Industry Consultant for *Diver* magazine.

John is married and has two grown up children. He now lives in Alverstoke, near Gosport in Hampshire, UK.

Other AquaPress titles:-

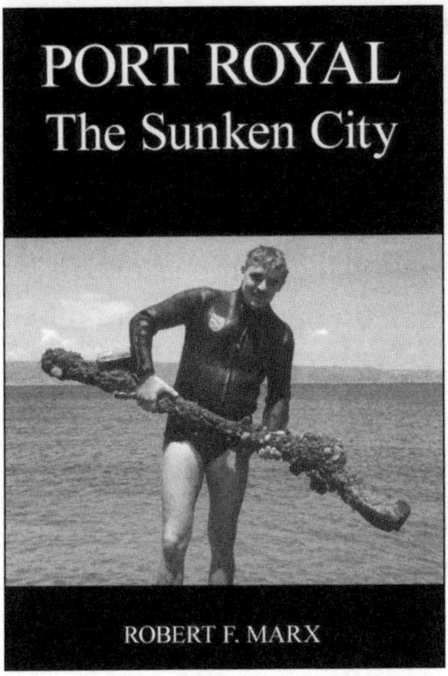

Port Royal

The Sunken City

by Robert F. Marx

In the seventeenth century, Port Royal was a legendary city, a city of vast wealth and pleasure-seeking, the home port of the buccaneers. Today, Port Royal is a city of legends, legends of the 1692 earthquake and tidal wave that caused the city to sink beneath the sea, and legends of the fortunes that may be buried there.

Robert F. Marx was one of the men caught up in those legends, and this book describes the fulfillment of his childhood dream: a two-and-a-half year exploration of the historic Jamaican port. The first investigation of the site by a trained marine archaeologist, his expedition discovered thousands of perfectly preserved artifacts of life in the 17th century city: silver and pewter ware; brass, iron and wooden tools; and much more, including two hoards of classic buried treasure: Spanish pieces of eight.

But Port Royal did not easily give up its treasures: working on a painfully slim budget, Marx and his rag-tag crew had to cope with murky, polluted waters, inhospitable sharks, eels and crabs; razorsharp coral and ancient walls on the verge of collapse; and the intractable opposition of some financial and political interests.

Blending real-life adventure, colourful history and the thrill of discovery, Marx has written a fascinating account of one of the most important marine archaeological expeditions ever undertaken.

ISBN: 978-0-9544060-1-1

Scapa Flow Dive Guide
2nd Ed.

by Lawson Wood

The most comprehensive guide to diving the reefs and wrecks of Scapa Flow. Scapa Flow has international acclaim as one of the top five wreck diving locations in the world and has more diveable wreckage than any other area in Europe. The shipwrecks are a mixture of battleships, cruisers and destroyers from the German High Seas Battle Fleet scuttled towards the end of WWI and the direct actions of the British Admiralty which sank a further 43 ships during both world conflicts to block the entrances to Scapa Flow.

- The definitive guide to diving Scapa Flow covering all wrecks and reef dives.
- Contains a wealth of previously unpublished material.
- Detailed descriptions of every dive including special conditions and unusual features.
- Includes highly detailed full colour maps of all wreck locations.
- Detailed historical accounts of all the wrecks.
- Bottom scans and line drawings of many of the wrecks.
- Suitable for all levels of experience from novice to ‘technical’ diver.

ISBN: 978-1905492114

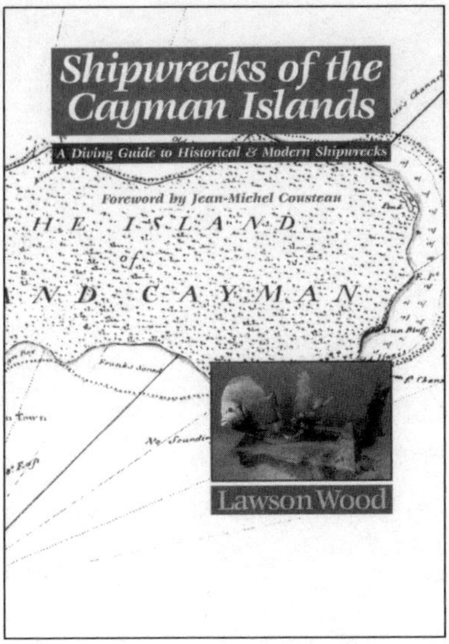

Shipwrecks of the Cayman Islands

A diving guide to historic & modern shipwrecks

by Lawson Wood

The definitive guide to exploring and diving the Shipwrecks of the Cayman Islands. The spectacular natural beauty of the islands hides a treacherous coastline that has seen many ships founder. For the first time in print, there is an accurate account of around 140 of the best-known and identified shipwrecks. This guide relates to how and where these ships have been lost and also gives important information on how to identify details on the various types of sailing vessel that have plied these waters over the last 500 years. Packed with over 200 photographs and illustrations this book will undoubtedly be used as the authoritative reference on how to dive and snorkel the most popular of these artificial reefs.

ISBN: 978-0954406035

For these and many more titles visit www.aquapress.co.uk